THE **A**-TEAM™ *

annual
1986

£3.25

CONTENTS

Copyright © MCMLXXXV by
Stephen J. Cannell Productions.
All rights reserved throughout the world.
Published in Great Britain by
World International Publishing Limited.
P.O. Box 111, Gt. Ducie Street, Manchester M60 3BL.
Printed in Italy
SBN 7235 6748 4

*a trademark of Stephen J. Cannell Productions and
licensed by Merchandising Corporation of America, Inc.

THE MILD MANNERED *MURDERER*

"Throw down your gun, Baracus! You're surrounded! It's the end of the line!"

Trapped down an alley, with a high wooden fence behind him and a warehouse on either side, B.A. snarled defiantly into the spotlight like a cornered animal. He knew his own weapon was empty.

"Ain't no sucker born gonna put me back inside!" he growled vehemently.

Standing by the spotlight as his men trained their weapons on the hapless ex-mechanic, Colonel Decker allowed himself a smile of satisfaction. "You've no choice, Sergeant," he called

out. "The Robin Hood pantomime is over. It's time to face up to what you really are. A deserter. A violent, insubordinate –"

Decker's tirade was interrupted by the hissing of four large axes thrown from behind him. They somersaulted through the air in quick succession, each one higher than the last, finally embedding themselves into the wooden fence above B.A.'s head. As Decker turned to see who had thrown them, a short burst of automatic fire exploded his spotlight in a puff of white smoke and sparks. All Decker could see when he

whirled round was a shadowy figure stepping quickly out of the line of fire.

"Shoot!" he yelled angrily. "Open fire!"

"On which target, sir?" asked his second in command. Decker pulled his own service revolver from its holster and fired six shots at the place where B.A. had been standing. When a second spotlight was finally made to work, Decker could see his efforts had been wasted. The alley was empty. B.A. had used the embedded axes as handholds and scrambled over the fence. A distant squeal of tyres and a muted chorus of *We'll*

5

Meet Again confirmed his worst fears. The A-Team had escaped him again.

"Where to, Hannibal?" asked Face, as B.A. settled down in the back of the A-Team truck.

Hannibal stopped singing and turned to Murdock. "You check out Kimberly Blair?" he asked. Murdock didn't answer. He sat staring straight ahead, his head absolutely still.

"Murdock?" Hannibal prompted.

"Don't want to move my lips," he explained through gritted teeth. "Got to keep my head absolutely level."

"Your fool head's 'bout as level as a paper cup in a storm at sea," B.A. interrupted.

"You're talking about inside, B.A.," Murdock went on. "It's the outside I'm worried about. If I lean my head just one itty bitty inch to either side, the clockwork train going round and round the rim of my sombrero is likely

to jump the tracks and take all the jelly baby passengers plunging to their tiny little dooms."

"You're not wearing a sombrero," Face pointed out.

Gingerly, Murdock patted the top of his head. "Well, I'll be a chipmunk's chum," he said with a smile. "Those walking onion rings from Venus are craftier than I thought."

"Kimberly Blair?" Hannibal reminded him, as Murdock peered into a matchbox and B.A. stared out of the window in apparent disgust.

"I told you not to send this peanut to check her out," he growled. "The crazy fool's done blown his manhole cover for good!"

"It's elementary, my dear Holmes," said Murdock, puffing an imaginary pipe. "Our friend Kimberly is the genuine article — a tax paying, law abiding air hostess. And pretty to boot. I checked with her employers and her friends, and her story stacks up. Maybe there's a pea under her mattress that stops her from sleeping all night but I didn't see it."

"You find out why she's scared?" asked Face, slowly turning the wheel as the A-Team truck slid through the cross-town traffic.

Murdock nodded. "Sure. She thinks somebody's trying to kill her."

"What about the police?"

"She reported one case of a suspected intruder and one case of dangerous driving. Both trails were colder than a night in the icebox. The cops are keeping an eye out for her, but they can't spare a man for full time protection." Murdock squinted through the front window into the night. "That's it, Face," he said, pointing. "The end house on the right."

Face pulled up and the A-Team got out. Hannibal was checking out the rear of the house when suddenly the cold night air was shattered by a terrified scream coming from inside.

B.A. was first to the door, smashing into it with his shoulder as he ran. The lock splintered, the hinges were torn from the frame and the door flew into the hallway with Face and Murdock tumbling after it. Round the back, Hannibal was climbing in through an open window. Face ran at the lounge door and hit it with a flying drop kick, and as B.A. and Murdock followed Face in they saw a very frightened Kimberly Blair fighting for her life against a small man with a clown's mask on his face and a carving knife in his hands.

come with me. We're going to nail that nasty little noodle."

"I say we cure him – permanently," growled B.A., racing out of the front doorway as further up the street the powerful engine of a yellow sedan roared into life. He jumped into the driver's seat of the van and was already gunning the motor when Hannibal and Murdock piled in. He let off the brakes, stepped on the accelerator, and the van squealed forward. The chase was on.

"If there's one thing I can't stand," muttered B.A., savagely twisting the wheel as the van

more in his locker than just a knife."

Murdock was right. As B.A. stepped on the gas and the A-Team van approached the limit of its speed, a hand came out of the sedan's window, waited for three seconds, then dropped a grenade.

When the door flew open he managed to push Kimberly roughly away, then spin quickly and hurl the knife straight at Murdock. Murdock ducked and the knife thwacked into the wall above the light switch, cutting the wires and plunging the room into darkness. Hannibal arrived in the doorway in time to hear the front window shattering as the assailant jumped out.

"Face – stay with Kimberly," he ordered. "Murdock, B.A. –

skidded round a sharp right turn, "it's some cheap trash punk acting big with a knife."

"He doesn't drive like a punk," observed Hannibal as the yellow sedan ignored the lights and weaved through the current of southbound traffic like an eel.

"And I'm not one to build up a garbageous pile of sub-human scum," said Murdock, as the A-Team van swerved to get closer, "but I reckon that slash-happy trash-head's got

B.A. hit the brakes and spun the wheel, but he wasn't quick enough. The grenade went off under the near side front tyre, lifting the van into the air and sending hot shards of metal ripping through the roof. Still rising, the van ploughed into a fire hydrant, rolled slowly over in the air, and came down heavily on its roof.

"Left! He's taken a left!" said Murdock as the van's momentum carried it hurtling forward with sparks flying from the roof,

7

the screeching sound of tortured metal howling in the night like a lovesick banshee.

"The tyres are treading air, Sergeant," said Hannibal as B.A. tugged furiously at the steering wheel. B.A. glared, then braced himself against the ceiling as the van drifted across the path of a startled taxi driver, slammed into the kerb, and rolled back upright. B.A. was reaching for the starter before he'd stopped bouncing back into his seat again.

"Deader than dog meat!" he rasped angrily, thumping the steering wheel with his fist. "That sneaky snake's done gone too far! That's one sucker who's gonna wish he'd stayed home counting the hairs on his hands!"

While B.A. spent the night working on the van, Hannibal and Murdock went back to Kimberly's house. She seemed fully recovered from her attack and was showing Face the latest dance steps she'd picked up on her last flight to Rio, when they came in.

"You OK?" asked Hannibal, flopping down in an armchair. Murdock squatted under the table.

"Sure," smiled Kimberly. "You boys saved my life. I don't know how I'll ever be able to pay you back."

"Some people say that's why money was invented," said Hannibal, lighting a cigar. "But we let that scumball get away, and that's bad for our reputation. And after what he did to the van, I don't think B.A.'s going to make him flavour of the month."

"That's right," Murdock piped up. "The needle on his mad-o-meter's bustin' the casing."

"So you've got us on your side," Face confirmed. "Now tell Hannibal what you told me."

Kimberly bit her lip and a frown formed on her face as she struggled to root out some memory from a hidden corner of her brain.

"I can't be certain... but when we were fighting, the mask slipped for a second... and... if I didn't know better, I could have sworn that it was Mr Mumms."

"You know this crummy screwball?" asked Hannibal.

Kimberly seemed unsure. "I only got a glimpse of him. Mr Mumms is a toy salesman. He often travels with our airline.

The funny thing is that I saw him recently – during a stopover at Memphis – and although I said hello – he walked right past me as though I wasn't there."

"Can you remember when this was?"

"Last Thursday, I think... No, it was Wednesday, definitely Wednesday."

Hannibal got to his feet and stretched like a waking cat. "You got any friends on the booking counter?" he asked.

Kimberly nodded.

"Good."

Hannibal went on, "Face, you stay here and ring up the airport. Check all of Mumms' movements. I'll call you back later. You and me, Murdock, are going into the newspaper business."

Hannibal and Murdock took a cab down to the local newspaper offices and called back from the lobby of the noisy, brightly lit multi-storey building. Kimberly's colleagues had come through. Hannibal jotted down a number of dates and destinations and then, while Murdock distracted a secretary by posing as a freelance reporter with a red hot story for sale, the

A-Team leader checked the newspaper files.

"What do you mean, you don't handle unsolicited material?" asked Murdock indignantly as the secretary anxiously shuffled some papers on her desk. "Isn't my track record good enough for you? Who broke 'The Worm that started a War'? Me – that's who. I've got a nose for news. Look at it! I can sniff out a story like a pig after truffles. Who do you think tracked down Jody, the rabbit that saved a family of six and who now lives in a cardboard box? Who made the vital link between the measles epidemic and the rash of Bigfoot sightings? And this one tops even that! It even caps 'Parachuting Pop Star in Peanut Peril Panic'. I'm beating the film people off with a club! I don't think I'm giving too much away when I say it involves a missing heiress, a shadowy underworld figure, the CIA, the KGB, the ABC –"

"What's the ABC?"

"Didn't they teach you anything at school? And you working for a newspaper too." He leaned forward across the desk and fixed her with his friendliest smile. "Still, you sure are pretty. Those eyes... they're like diamonds made of sky. And those lashes are like Japanese fans. Don't blink too much or that fly in the corner will get blown into the wall. And that hair..."

"Just leave your name and I'm sure the editor will contact you," said the secretary coolly as Hannibal returned.

"Never mind, Ace," he said as he and Murdock walked to the lift. "That's the way the cake mix crumbles in the fast lane world of selling advertising space."

"I guess you're right," said Murdock, stepping into the lift. "Did you score?"

"Murdock," beamed Hannibal as the lift doors hissed shut. "I think we just hit the crackpot jackpot."

Early the next morning, as Ernest Mumms appeared for work at his toy shop, he was not particularly surprised to see what looked like a film crew setting up to shoot a car chase. He felt a little uneasy when he saw the lead van in the chase was remarkably similar to the one that had followed him the night before, and, when it smashed through the front of his shop window, he reached inside his pocket for his gun.

"Smile," said a voice behind him and Mumms turned to see Hannibal pointing what at first sight looked like a hand-held camera right at his face. A second glance revealed it to be a cardboard box with an Uzi machine pistol inside it. "That's right, buddy, you're on camera.

You want me to start shooting the first scene?"

"I... I..." Mumms looked nervously around. B.A. and Murdock had climbed out of the van and were giving away the toys inside to a gathering crowd of children. "That man's stealing my toys!"

"I wouldn't let him hear you talk that way, you crazy creepy crawly," said Hannibal. "He's tough. He drinks blood from rusty cans and sleeps in a barbed wire hairnet. And he's mean. The man's got a bad attitude. Apart from which, he spent all night repairing that van, and he doesn't work cheap."

"I've no idea what you're talking about," Mumms lied.

Hannibal laughed. "We

checked you out, Mumms. The toy shop is just a cover. You were in Memphis when Johnny the Wolf got wiped out. You were in Chicago when Kid Bones popped his socks. And you were in the Big Apple when Alabama Moonshine bought his one way ticket to the Home for Obsolete Hoodlums. You may pose as a mild mannered mouse, but I've seen you come out of the phone booth. You're a mob killer, Mumms. A contract assassin who helps the big boys keep their troops in line. And when you got spotted by Kimberly in Memphis you figured

she might catch your action, so you decided to rub her out too."

"This is preposterous!"

"Isn't it just? And what's even more amazing is that someone as smart as Johnny the Wolf's brother should have believed the story when I told it to him."

Mumms' face drained of all colour. "You told Jimmy the Jackal I killed Johnny?" he gasped.

Hannibal nodded. "Nothing personal, of course. He seemed quite angry. Mind you, he wasn't as mad as Papa Bones. I thought the phone would melt

when I gave him your address. And Alabama's wife – do you know Wildcat Winnie? – well, all I got from her was a loud meow, a wild scratching sound and then the line went dead."

"But... but... they'll kill me!" said Mumms.

Hannibal kept on nodding. "Most probably," he said, reaching into Mumms' pocket and removing his gun. "Of course there's always a chance that they'll just slap you on the wrist with a rolled up newspaper, but –" Hannibal stopped nodding and was beginning to shake his head when Face called out from his look-out post at the corner of the street.

"Big black limo coming up. Five men in. Out of town plates."

"Please!" shrieked Mumms. "Please! You gotta help me!"

Hannibal's smile vanished. "On your way, scumbag!" he snarled menacingly. "Find yourself a cop to make famous!"

Mumms didn't need telling twice. He sprinted to the end of the street and began waving down a black and white as B.A., Murdock and Hannibal loaded his abandoned toys into the van.

"Snap it up, you guys!"

warned Face from the corner. "We got company!"

"You can drop the act now, Face," said Hannibal. "Mumms has turned himself in."

"It's no act, Hannibal!" puffed Face, sprinting for the van. "It's Decker!"

They threw the last of the toys into the back of the van and sped off. As B.A. steered through a narrow gap between the parked black and white and an oncoming jeep, Face turned round and studied the toys in the back. Murdock was whispering to a fluffy pink crocodile.

"Exactly how much did we earn for this deal?" Face asked Hannibal.

Hannibal felt inside his pocket. "Roughly two hundred dollars," he replied, counting a small wad of bills, "though when you smooth it out it's nearer twenty nine dollars three cents."

"How much do you think we'll get for the toys?"

"Ain't selling the toys," B.A. grunted. "We're gonna give them to the kids."

"Fine sentiments, B.A.," said Hannibal, slapping his ex-sergeant on the shoulder. "What do you say, Murdock?"

"Well..." drawled Murdock. "My heart says yes, my mind says, 'What's happening?', I haven't heard yet from my kidney, and my big toe says –"

"Ain't selling those toys!" B.A. repeated fiercely. "We're giving them to the kids, you dig?"

"You know, B.A.," said Face, smiling. "For a man who gets sick licking an airmail stamp you can be pretty –"

"Ain't sellin' those toys!" yelled B.A., standing on the brake. Behind them the sound of Decker's men could be heard getting closer. B.A. looked slowly round at the rest of his smiling companions with a face like an angry bulldog. "You dig?" he asked quietly. They dug. B.A. hit the accelerator.

The kids at the care centre were in for one heck of a party.

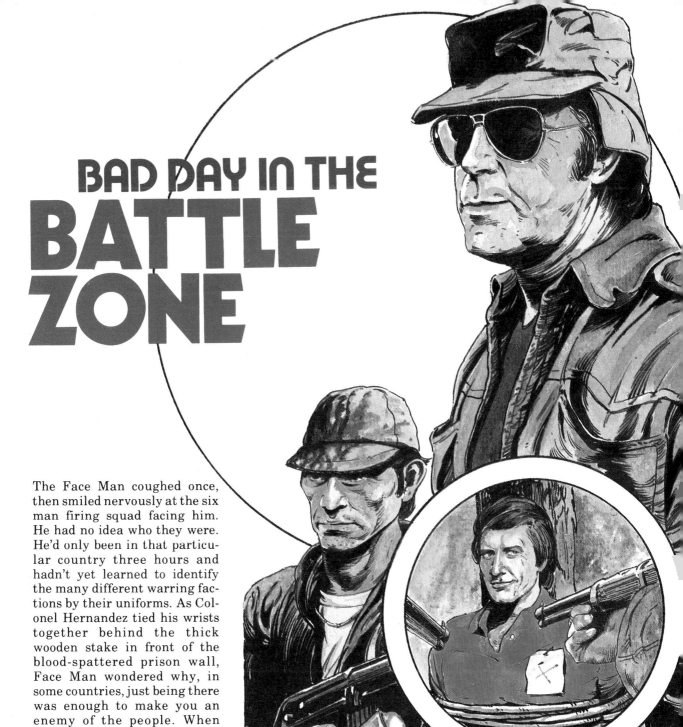

BAD DAY IN THE BATTLE ZONE

The Face Man coughed once, then smiled nervously at the six man firing squad facing him. He had no idea who they were. He'd only been in that particular country three hours and hadn't yet learned to identify the many different warring factions by their uniforms. As Colonel Hernandez tied his wrists together behind the thick wooden stake in front of the blood-spattered prison wall, Face Man wondered why, in some countries, just being there was enough to make you an enemy of the people. When Hernandez produced a red blindfold he shook his head.

"No thanks – it clashes with my shirt. And anyway, I don't want to miss the show."

"Very well," said Hernandez stiffly. "Do you have any last requests?"

"I think I'll sit this one out if you don't mind," smiled Face. "But do feel free to whistle a happy tune. And if any of your boys want to strut their funky stuff it's OK by me."

Hernandez drew his sword from his purple scabbard and held it up in the air as his men lifted their Kalashnikov AK-47s to their shoulders.

"Ready..." he began. Face Man searched the clear blue skies for any sign of the rest of the A-Team. There was none. "Aim..."

At the very moment Colonel Hernandez made to bring his sword down with the order to fire, two small black shapes looped into the yard and landed at his feet. Before he could even recognise them as grenades a military glider skimmed silently across the wall behind Face Man. The hold door was

11

kicked out and Hannibal appeared at the opening, a blazing M3 machine gun smoking and chattering in his hands. The firing squad scattered, the grenades went off, and the glider ploughed into the ground by two choppers.

As Hannibal began dragging a heavy sack towards one of the choppers Murdock covered him with a pair of colt 45s with mother-of-pearl handles. "Hey, Facy-boy!" he yelled across the square. "Cut out the ballroom dancing and sashay over here! We're moving out!"

"I'm not dancing, Murdock. I'm tied to a stake," explained Face.

"Ain't no time to argue — bring her with you!"

Face sighed, grasped the stake with both hands and pulled. The stake held fast. Face Man pushed and pulled, swaying from side to side, until the ground loosened up a bit, then he slid down the stake, grabbed it near the bottom, and pulled upwards. The stake came clear of the ground and, with it still tied to his back, Face sprinted across the yard to where Murdock was starting up the chopper. Already Hernandez' troops had recovered from the surprise attack and were laying down a steady bombardment.

"Hi, there. What's cooking, good looking?" smiled Murdock to the stake on Face Man's back. "I like your style. How's about teaching me a few moves?"

"It can't dance, Murdock," Face calmly insisted as Murdock took the chopper up. "It's a stake. Hannibal, can you help me out of these knots?"

Hannibal drew a bowie knife from his belt and cut easily through the cord binding Face's wrists. Below them they could see Hernandez piling into the second helicopter to give chase. As the chopper lifted off, Face Man took the stake and threw it downwards like a gigantic spear. It smashed through the whirring rotors and the stricken chopper fell heavily to the ground.

"Mighty cruel thing to do," remarked Murdock. "Just because she couldn't dance."

A sudden movement in the back made Face Man turn. There was something alive in the bag Hannibal had transferred from the glider. A bandaged hand appeared over the top of the bag, followed by a head and a neck, all completely covered in bandages. A muffled voice came from underneath. "I can't see a thing! Where am I?"

"Sssh!" hissed Hannibal. "We're on our way to hospital to bust the professor out. You've had one of your black-outs. We've dressed you up as a patient. There's no way you could pass as a doctor."

"How come I can't see? And that sound. If we're in a chopper you're gonna wish I was a doctor, 'cause I'm going to teach you pain from the inside."

"We're not in a chopper, B.A.," lied Face, frantically signalling for Murdock to set them down by two jeeps below them. "We're in a jeep. Now get back in that bag and stay quiet. We're coming to a road block."

Murdock put the chopper safely down and they transferred B.A. into the back of one of the jeeps. Hannibal took out

three white coats from the front seat and handed them round. Murdock took the wheel while Hannibal and Face sat on either side of B.A. who, squirming restlessly like a bear-sized mummy, was muttering angrily to himself under his bandages.

"The professor's at an old fortified castle that's being used as a hospital," Hannibal explained. "I see you didn't manage to steal us a tank."

"They jumped me when I was making up my mind between a brown and green one and a green and brown one. Those guys wouldn't believe I was just a simple shoe salesman who'd taken a wrong turn on Highway 64."

"Heck, I wouldn't believe you if you said the sky was green," said Murdock, turning round and grinning as the jeeps sped past some bullet scarred barns,

standing abandoned in the sun.

"It isn't," said Hannibal, placing some binoculars to his eyes and trying to focus them on the old castle on the top of the hill.

Murdock slapped the wheel and laughed out loud. "You're just as bad, Hannibal! Next you'll be telling us that the Eiffel Tower's in Paris!"

Hannibal didn't bother. He was too busy studying the defences of the castle. Although from a distance it reminded him of a shoebox with four large candles, one on each corner, there was no doubt that its positioning and design made it a virtually impregnable fortress. Built on the side of a gaping, plunging chasm, the only way it could be approached was by the road they were on, and the wide dirt strip gave the people in the castle at least five miles of uninterrupted firing. Hannibal refocussed as he swept the bat-

tlements with his binoculars. He stopped and grinned when he saw a uniformed figure standing by a manned mortar, focussing a pair of binoculars in the direction of the jeep.

"What do you think, Hannibal?" asked Face Man. "Are we going in to bat?"

"We're going in to bat, team," Hannibal replied. "And for this one we're going to have to play so far above ourselves our noses are going to bleed."

"You better cut the jive from this plan, Hannibal!" B.A. warned through his bandages.

"Plan?" said Hannibal, finally taking the binoculars from his eyes and giving a friendly wave to the men on the castle battlements. "Who said anything about a plan?"

When they pulled up at the castle gates, the battlements bristled with soldiers aiming rifles at them. There was the

his stompin' time!"

The reply was a bazooka shell that whistled above their heads and through an open door behind them. There was a thunderous roar and the shock wave carried a whirlwind of broken tables, candlesticks, paper and glass flying back at the jeep.

"Yeee-haw!" screamed Murdock, climbing out of the driver's seat. "They're throwing everything at us but that white enamel thing that's designed for peeling potatoes and sailing toy boats and doing the washing up and stuff. You know – there's two twiddly things on top where water comes out and a hole at the bottom where –"

"We get your drift, Murdock," said Hannibal, leading them towards some stairs. "And if they do throw the kitchen sink at us, just make sure you catch it and throw it right back at them."

With Hannibal in the lead and B.A. covering the back, they fought their way along damp, half-lit passages, up narrow winding stairs, through sparsely furnished hallways, until they came to a half open door. Inside the elegant room a man with a stethoscope was bending over a tired looking figure who Hannibal immediately recognised as Professor Johnson, the brilliant chemist whose company had hired the A-Team to rescue.

"Stand back, doc," ordered Hannibal, grabbing the man's arm as he pulled out an HK630 from his pocket. He forced the man's hand upwards and as the two grappled fiercely 63mm slugs slammed into the ceiling, rattling the ornate chandelier and bringing down showers of plaster and dust. B.A. ended the contest by stepping forward and dropping the man with a short right that caught him full on the jaw.

"You OK?" asked Face.

"Sure," replied the Professor. "But you got here just in time.

sound of a bolt slipping back from behind the huge wooden doors, and when they swung slowly open the A-Team found themselves face to face with a rusting M4 Sherman tank.

Standing in front of the tank was a tall soldier in a colourful uniform, flanked by two grey-looking men in white coats. Murdock gulped uneasily.

"Gotta wounded man," said Hannibal, stepping from the jeep and pointing at B.A.'s bandaged body. "Needs help pretty bad. You going to let us in?"

"Of course," replied the leader, waving the jeep inside the courtyard. "Come in, come in. We are only too pleased to welcome such illustrious visitors as Colonel Hannibal Smith and the A-Team." His smile grew suddenly cold. "What a pity we can't let you leave here alive!"

The doors of the courtyard started closing behind them as the men on the battlements took aim. Face Man stood up on his seat and loosed off a full clip, peppering the walls, forcing the soldiers to duck and causing ricochets to zing across the square. Murdock threw the jeep into gear and stomped the accelerator and Hannibal dived back in the jeep, took two short fuse grenades and threw them at the nearest door. The blast knocked the thick panelled slab of oak off its hinges and Murdock flattened it as he raced through the narrow gap. B.A. pulled some of the bandages from around his eyes and picked up a discarded Franchi LF57 submachine gun.

"Better stay away from that door, suckers!" he warned, aiming a short blast at the opening. "Because this fool's behind on

That guy was going to kill me. He's Sam Gluckner – the torture expert."

"You strong enough to travel?" asked Hannibal, striding through the open window onto the balcony. The Professor nodded in reply. Hannibal peered over the balustrade as the Face Man came up to join him. Below them, the castle wall stretched down until it met the sheer face of the cliff, falling away several hundred feet to the dry riverbed below. Directly opposite them, the other canyon wall seemed to glow in the evening sun, the small clumps of bushes clinging to its surface casting long shadows against the red rock face.

"Anything left in the tank marked 'genius'?" asked Face. "Or should I start sewing a white flag?"

Hannibal rubbed his chin as he turned from the balcony and gazed back into the room. Murdock was covering the door, B.A. was unravelling his bandages and the Professor was slumped in a chair, staring at the back of his hands. Slowly, a smile began to form on Hannibal's face.

"You know, Face," he began, "I love it when –"

Hannibal's voice was cut short by a loud burst of rapid fire from the door.

"Are any of you expecting guests?" asked Murdock, crouching by the open doorway with his back flat against the wall. When nobody bothered to reply he jumped to his feet and let go another shuddering burst. "I thought not," he said, swiftly reloading, "and these non-com noodles don't look the type who'd want to play spin the bottle."

"You got a plan, Hannibal?" asked B.A., scowling as the A-Team leader smiled and patted his cheek.

"Sure I got a plan, B.A.," he replied. "And it's so good that if it had two ugly sisters they wouldn't let it go to the ball."

"What are we gonna do?"

"Do?" repeated Hannibal, pointing upwards as Murdock's protracted burst of firing drove yet another batch of soldiers back. "Why, we're going to pull down the chandelier, of course."

"I said I ain't in no mood for no jive!"

"I'm not jazzin' you, B.A. Here's what we're gonna do..."

"I'm afraid we ain't got a lot of time to do anything, Hannibal," Murdock butted in. "I'm clean out of ammo."

Hannibal handed Murdock his last clip. B.A. gave him two grenades. The Professor tossed him Gluckner's pistol.

"Make them count," said Hannibal.

Murdock grinned. "By the time I've finished with them, they'll be doing logarithms."

But, although Murdock used the ammunition as sparingly as he possibly could, and supplemented his firepower with a series of loud imitations of gunfire, his luck was out. One of the grenades failed to go off and the other had been thrown back at

him. By this time he kicked it out and slammed the door after it, there was no ammunition left.

"We still need more time," said Hannibal as the explosion rattled the thick door. "Negotiate with them."

"He's got nothing at all to negotiate with, Hannibal," Face Man pointed out as he came through the adjoining door with a large roll of electrical cable.

Hannibal smiled. "You know what the man said, Face. 'Sometimes nothing's a very cool hand'."

"You got it, Hannibal," said Murdock, pounding on the closed door. "Hey, you out there!" he shouted. "Come in with your hands up! This is your last chance to surrender!"

Murdock held out for three minutes. In that time Hannibal, B.A. and Face had pulled down the chandelier, stripped all excess weight from its frame, and fashioned it into a grappling hook. They had fastened

this to the cable, and now B.A. was whirling it round and round his head on the balcony in a bid to reach the other side of the canyon.

"They've rumbled me, boys," called Murdock from the door. "They're coming in."

"Here," said the Professor, dragging Gluckner's semi-conscious body to his feet. "This should hold them a bit."

Murdock smiled in admiration. While he had been confusing the soldiers, the Professor had taken B.A.'s bandages and wrapped them round Gluckner.

Murdock turned back to the door. "Okay! Okay!" he called as the shuffling sounds outside grew closer. "I'm sending somebody out!"

He opened the door and pushed Gluckner's bandaged body out. The soldiers, thinking it was B.A., immediately jumped on him, knocking him to the ground and handcuffing his hands behind his back.

Before the soldiers realised their mistake, the real B.A., with one final, muscle-wrenching flourish, had spun twice on the balls of his feet, jumped forward and released the chandelier. As the mighty ex-mechanic teetered on the edge of the balcony, the stripped down chandelier curved gracefully through the air, floating across the canyon with the electric cable trailing behind.

Hannibal pulled B.A. back from the brink and they watched for what seemed like minutes as the chandelier kept going, gliding and falling, with the whistling of the uncoiling cable seeming to drown the muffled banging on the door behind them. Then the chandelier hit home on the steep slope with a red puff of dust, fell ten feet into a tangle of roots, rolled slightly to one side, and stuck firm.

"Let's get this end tight," ordered Hannibal briskly, pul-

ling on the electrical cable as Murdock and the professor piled wardrobes, tables and chairs against the door. The man-made mountain of furniture was beginning to sway and tumble when Face Man looped an empty ammo belt over the cable, grabbed both ends tightly and jumped. The cable sagged and shuddered, but it held, and when Face reached the other side, Murdock set off, with the Professor clinging to his back. They slid safely across and Hannibal turned to B.A. on the balcony, as behind them the door was splintering open. "Your turn, Sergeant," said Hannibal sternly. "And that's an order!"

B.A. sighed, then let rip with a roundhouse right that knocked Hannibal off his feet and onto his back. "I guess you forgot about my attitude," he muttered, slinging Hannibal over his shoulder, throwing his spent cartridge belt over the cable, then jumping. They had almost reached the other side when the soldiers burst in and shot through the cable.

B.A. and Hannibal dropped together, landing heavily on the side of the steep slope and tumbling for twenty feet before coming to a stop. By the time the rest of them caught up, B.A. was already on his feet, brushing the dirt from his clothes, and Hannibal was sitting up, rubbing his jaw, his cigar still clamped between his teeth. "Anyone get the licence number?" he asked. "Sergeant, when you hit a man you make sure he remembers it."

"When I really hit a man," said B.A., helping Hannibal to his feet, "he's through remembering."

Hannibal smiled as he fingered the swelling on his face. "I can well believe that, Sergeant," he said. "But now the show's over and we're moving out. It's time to go home."

"Hannibal," grinned Face as they trudged towards the border, "that's the only good plan you've had today."

IN SEARCH OF THE SEVEN GOLDEN ORCHIDS

In the main hall of the Veterans' Hospital a travelling ballet troupe was approaching the climax of their performance of *Swan Lake* when Murdock first stood up on his front row seat.

"There's something wrong with the microphones!" he complained loudly. "I can't hear a word they're saying!"

Within seconds, rookie nurse Debbie Parsons was at his side, trying to calm him down. "It's all right," she said soothingly. "There's no talking in ballet."

Murdock feigned a righteous indignation. "No talking?! What kind of cheap show is this? I should have guessed what was going on when they started walking around on their toes. I've nothing against small people but if the part calls for a clod-hopping giant, then the pitter patter of tiny feet just isn't going to cut it. An' there's something wrong with the underfloor heating, too. They're

hopping about like fleas. And that man with the funny trousers is so bow-legged I bet he scrapes the wallpaper off his living room – both sides at once. He'd probably be big enough for the part if he'd have them straightened. I wasn't expecting Cecil B. but this is just –"

"Please!" hissed Nurse Parsons, taking a firm grip on his arm. "You're upsetting the dancers!"

Murdock looked around. The ballet dancers were bravely ignoring him while the other Vets were grinning their encouragement. Suddenly Murdock stiffened, pointed to the stage and let out a long, eardrum withering, blood churning howl. "It's there!" he yelled, leaping over the orchestra pit and onto the stage. "It's come at last! It's the great Giant Gerbil himself!"

He rushed past the dancers and disappeared behind the

scenery, reappearing seconds later with a mop head in his hand. He held it up to the light and shook his head in wonder. "It's Gonzo! It really is! The Giant Green Gerbil! I can hardly believe it! A giant furry rodent fully twenty feet across! Sent here by Hokumscope from planet X – just as the legend predicted! From now on –"

But Murdock was cut off by the arrival of three orderlies who pushed their way through the dancers and grabbed him. They were carrying him off stage, with Nurse Parsons in the lead, when Face stepped out of the wings, dressed in a military uniform. "I hope you're not going to take that man away and sedate him," he said sternly, flashing credentials briefly in the nurse's face.

"Is there any alternative?" she answered exasperatedly as Murdock struggled, still holding the mop head.

"I believe there is," said Face, holding her by the arm and looking deep into her eyes. "We've been looking for some time to find a suitable patient on which to test the theories of Smith."

"Smith?"

"Smith. Dr Smith believes that certain phrenological corpuscular hydrangeas, index linked biochemically with subcutaneous acupuncture, can nullify the coffee and doughnut syndrome with the vacuum cleaner effect."

"What on earth are you talking about?"

"I didn't say it was easy, nurse, but if there's one chance it might work, we've got to take it. Dr Smith believes that if this man was allowed, of his own accord, to go unattended to the chief administrator's office and try to explain exactly what he was thinking, then perhaps – just perhaps, mind – the oligarchial nature of his post hysterical bleep structure rectangle might transmogrify the ossification of the microcircuits inflation proof data in a tri-lateral compound geolithic abracadabra of his cranium and could – always accepting the random factor – completely cure this brave airman for good."

"But, but –" Nurse Parsons was hesitant.

Murdock started howling.

Face grabbed his head and began feeling it for bumps. "You've got to be brave, nurse. Decisive! You've got to hurl the gauntlet of science into the face of bureaucracy! Look at his eyes! Already the intense multiflexity of his neurological quark modules are over-stimulating his bumptious gland. His periferal intusions are positively bustaceous! These are the classic symptoms of Smith's syndrome. I'm telling you, nurse – this man is sick!"

"Well, I –"

"Good! That's settled then," said Face, pushing Murdock through the side door. "I'll take him to the chief administrator immediately!"

As they ran through the grounds to the outer wall, Murdock looked at Face with new respect. "I never knew you had such an excellent grasp of the language of quackery," he said. "If I was a duck I'd be jealous!"

"Knock it off and keep running, pal," smiled Face. "If the men with the butterfly nets catch up with us we'll both be ripe for a spell in the rubber room."

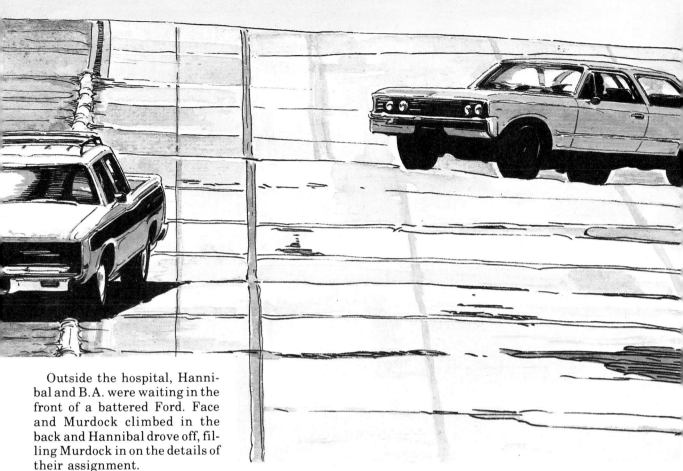

Outside the hospital, Hannibal and B.A. were waiting in the front of a battered Ford. Face and Murdock climbed in the back and Hannibal drove off, filling Murdock in on the details of their assignment.

"We're after seven golden orchids," he began. "Somebody ripped them off from our client's museum and left imitations in their place. B.A. got a lead on one of their security men, John Dancer. We're on our way to see him now. Any questions?"

"This John Dancer," asked Murdock. "Does he drive a red and yellow Chevy with whitewall tyres?"

"Yeah – how did you know?"

"I didn't, but there's a vehicle answering that description been tailing us since we left the hospital."

B.A. turned round and Hannibal studied his mirror.

"He's right, Hannibal," said B.A. "It's Dancer. And he looks like he's hired some help."

"No sweat, Sergeant," said Hannibal, taking a sharp right. The Chevy followed. "Face, I think it's time to break out the ammunition."

Face coughed. "I was meaning to tell you about that, Hannibal," he grinned anxiously. "Only my contact didn't arrive in time, so I left orders for him to store the guns in the back of Tony's delicatessen."

"That's only two blocks from –"

"Get your heads down, suckers!" B.A. interrupted. "Those fools gonna start shooting!"

Hannibal swerved and the rest ducked down as John Dancer leaned out of the window of his car and opened up with a burst from an automatic rifle. The back window of the Ford caved in, showering Face and Murdock with glass. Hannibal stepped on the gas. "When we get to Tony's he said, racing to beat the lights at the next intersection, "you three fall out and get yourself some edge. I'll put these dog's breath dingbats on a platter for you."

"How?" asked Face, his forehead pressed hard to the back seat as another burst from behind raked the speeding car.

Hannibal grinned. "Didn't you ever see me in *Frankenstein Versus the Murderous Moonshiners*?" he asked.

"No."

"No matter," said Hannibal as the car squealed round a corner. "Hit it!"

Face went first, hitting the doorhandle with his elbow and rolling out of the car and under a parked truck. Murdock followed him at the same time as B.A. jumped, and the two of them rolled over and over together until they came to a halt among some rubbish bags at the side of Tony's. Hannibal had closed the doors before the Chevy followed them round the corner.

"OK, Smith," he smiled to himself as the Chevy gave

chase. "Let's see how good a stunt man you really are."

Hannibal gunned the motor as the Ford raced along the empty street. When the needle passed sixty he went into action, utilising all his hard earned knowledge from the tougher side of the movie business. He suddenly threw the gearstick into neutral, stood on the brakes and cut the wheel to the left. The Ford began spinning into what would have been a perfect 180° turn if the wheels had stayed on the road, but the car's velocity was so high that it flipped over and began rolling over and over, sideways, down the street. By this time Hannibal, flung across the seat towards the passenger door by the first swerve, had dived under the dashboard and was riding it out as the roof caved in and the remaining windows shattered. The buffeting, thundering storm of action finally subsided and the wrecked Ford came to a halt in the forecourt of a disused garage.

Seconds later, John Dancer's Chevvy pulled up alongside. "There's no way those fools could walk from that one," said Dancer with grim satisfaction, studying the crumpled doors and almost totally flattened roof. The two other men in the car with him nodded as they got out to inspect the damage. The three men had walked round the wreck twice before they began to suspect something was very badly wrong.

"There's nobody in it!" said Dancer, disbelievingly.

"Right first time!" came a voice from inside. Dancer peered in through a narrow crack where the window should have been and just as his eyes were beginning to focus on Hannibal's smiling features staring up from under the dashboard, a harsh voice from behind cut right across his increasingly confused thoughts.

"Looks like you three snake-eyes, suckers!"

The three men turned to see B.A., Face and Murdock

silhouetted against the street lights, machine guns glinting dully in their hands. Dancer cast a despairing glance towards the Chevy, where his own weapon lay on the front seat. Hannibal kicked open the twisted door of the Ford and flipped his cigar into the gutter. He took two pairs of handcuffs thrown by Murdock, and with B.A. prodding Dancer's men with his rifle, walked the hoods over to a petrol pump. Murdock and Face waited while Hannibal spoke to the men in hushed tones, and ten minutes later, with Dancer and his cronies handcuffed to the pump, the A-Team was on its way to Aspen, Colorado in the red and yellow Chevy with Hannibal relaxing in the back.

"I love it when a plan comes together," he smiled. "Now do any of you guys know how to hot-dog?"

"You mean eating or skiing?" asked Face.

"Skiing."

"That's easy," said Murdock. "You put the mustard on last."

The following evening, at the top of a steep, snow covered hill flanking a valley outside Aspen, Colorado, the A-Team stood in their ski suits listening carefully as Hannibal went through his last minute instructions.

"Dancer said that a guy named Mudflats O'Donoghue is holding the orchids. He's a billionaire with an I.Q. somewhere between a ball of mud and a cocktail stick. He also thinks that people are out to get him, so he surrounds himself with a bunch of no-neck numskulls with itchy trigger fingers. That's his hidey hole there." Hannibal pointed to an imposing ranch-style mansion at the bottom of the valley. "He could have hidden the orchids anywhere so we've got to grab Mudflats and make him spill. The best way of doing that –"

Suddenly the snow around them started jumping up and

down, holes appeared in the trees, and then the sound of chattering machine guns reached their ears, backed up by the growing roar of a Piper PA-22 Tri-Pacer as it plunged from the low clouds and sped straight towards them, the two machine guns mounted on its wings spitting red hot slugs of lead.

"Spread out!" Hannibal ordered, slipping the catch on his Uzi. "We'll regroup outside the house!" He knelt down and opened fire as the plane whooshed overhead. When the grenades started falling he picked up his spare ammo, launched himself into the air and set out after the others.

By the time the Piper had circled and was coming in for its second run, Hannibal had caught them up. He was about to order them to fan out even more when first B.A., then Murdock and Face, skiied to a halt. Hannibal did the same,

curving to a sudden stop in a flurry of snow.

"Never did fancy getting shot down in the back," said Murdock, taking aim at the low flying plane.

"You said it, fool," B.A. agreed, opening fire. "Come and get it, suckers!"

The four men stood their ground against the hurtling Tri-Pacer, pouring on the firepower as the plane's high calibre slugs kicked up the snow around them. There was a cloud of smoke, a belch of orange flame, and the stricken Piper pulled suddenly upward and roared off into the clouds, its engines screaming as it climbed into the sky.

"Reckon that's the last we'll see of that particular species of flying ant," said Murdock as they all reloaded their weapons.

When B.A. had finished, his face suddenly took on a puzzled expression and he cupped his hand to his ear. "Wrong again,

sucker," he said fiercely. "It's coming back!"

The A-Team members threw themselves down in the snow as the Tri-Pacer, now pilotless and out of control, skimmed over their heads, scattering burning pieces of fuselage.

Hannibal was first to his feet as it soared aimlessly upward again. "They must have bailed out!" he said, starting off down the hill again at speed. "Forget the plan – we're going straight in!"

And with the badly damaged Tri-Pacer swooping round the sky like a drunken albatross, the A-Team skiied for all they were worth, gathering speed as they whistled over the snow towards the mansion.

Inside the mansion, Mudflats O'Donoghue was licking his lips in anticipation of his usual seven course meal. The noise from outside only confirmed in his mind that the troublesome mercenaries from L.A. had finally met their match. He tucked his towel sized napkin into the neck of his shirt and sat back for a brief moment to savour the sight of the fourteen foot long table in front of him, piled high with delicious food. He was reaching for a quail's egg when the glass window of his dining room shattered and Hannibal flew in through the air, still on his skis. He landed on the end of the table and skidded along it, spilling soups, meats, fish, rice, custard, vegetables, wines, forks, knives, spoons and plates before coming to a sudden halt when his skis smashed against Mudflats' chair, one on either side of the startled glutton's head. Hannibal stuck his Uzi in Mudflats' face, as the rest of the A-Team followed him in.

"The seven golden orchids, spinach brain!" he asked. "Where are they?"

"You heard him, Jack!" urged B.A., spraying the ceiling with a short burst that brought the ornate chandelier crashing

down on the centre of the table. "Talk fast!"

Mudflats' jowls wobbled from side to side as he tried to work out what was happening. The sound of a distant explosion followed by a low rumbling sound that seemed to be growing louder did nothing to help him concentrate.

"Better make that superfast, budgie brain," said Face, looking out of the window. "Something tells me that plane's crashed and started an avalanche!"

Mudflats tried to talk but the words wouldn't come. The rumbling was getting even louder when the butler walked in carrying the orchids. He threw them at Hannibal who caught them with his free hand.

"If you got a cellar, get everyone in it!" warned Hannibal, dragging Mudflats to his feet and pushing him towards the butler. "We'll send the Red Cross in later!"

He took off his skis as Mudflats was led to the cellar, then he raced outside and started up Mudflats' customised Rolls Royce. The others joined him and Hannibal put his foot down, slamming through the perimeter fence and onto the road. They were doing sixty in five seconds and by the time the avalanche engulfed the mansion the needle was touching one hundred. It had reached one twenty on the speedo before the Rolls disappeared into the safety of a tunnel.

"Okay, then," said Hannibal, turning round in time to see the tumbling wave of snow block the tunnel entrance behind them. "Is anybody hurt?"

Murdock's voice came up from the tangle of arms and legs in the back. "As soon as I find my head I'll let you know."

Back at the Veterans' Hospital, Murdock was trying to sneak up to his room when Nurse Schneider suddenly appeared at the top of the stairs. "Where have you been?" she demanded icily. "Nurse Parsons told me all about your ridiculous antics with the mop. Gonzo the Giant Green Gerbil, was it?"

"Don't blame Nurse Parsons. It was my fault. I had to go see the chief administrator."

"Is that why you're wearing skis?"

Murdock looked down and grinned sheepishly. "It was Dr Smith's idea. He said that my pulmonary bi-pedal jack-in-the-box –"

"Don't give me any of that stupid gobbledegook!" snapped Nurse Schneider. "Did you see the chief administrator?"

"Yes – and I took this with me!" Murdock pulled the mop-head from out of his jacket.

"And?"

"Well, the chief administrator pointed out that giant green gerbils aren't usually used for washing floors. He also drew my attention to the fact that this object isn't twenty feet across..." Murdock looked sadly at the mophead in his hand and then suddenly his face brightened. "Mind you," he went on. "The chief administrator was very sympathetic. He said for a second he thought it was Gonzo himself when he first saw it!"

EXIT THE DRAGON

Tito B. Switch, Mammoth Studio's erratic pet genius and the creative intelligence behind *Pool Ghoul, Video Boneyard,* and *The Deadly Clams,* had always accepted that life, in some measure, must be a gamble. However, as he looked from the front door of his house to the back, he found himself wondering why fate had chosen that particular moment to deal him a handful of jokers then sneak up behind him with a roll of pennies in a sock. A man who already had two entries in *The World's Hundred Worst Films* just didn't deserve it. Out the back of his house was a film crew waiting to start shooting. Out the front was a platoon of military police ready to do the same. The film crew wanted the last reel of *Pool Ghoul II* in the can. The MPs, for some reason, wanted the guy in the ghoul suit in a military slammer at Fort Bragg. Meanwhile, as Tito Switch tried to argue the army out of doing anything too hasty, as his filmcrew stood chatting round the poolside out back, and as his latest discovery, the simmering, sultry Renata Ramirez, floated around on an airbed in front of the motionless cameras, looking bored, the ghoul, unaware of surface developments, sat on the bottom of Switch's swimming pool wondering why the rest of the A-Team hadn't got back to him after checking out the Chinaman.

"Okay, people," yelled Switch through a megaphone as he appeared at the glass doors that opened onto the poolside. "As you can see, we got changes." Behind him, soldiers were streaming out in two columns and taking up positions around the pool. "Up to now it's been the good ole boys from Devil's Bend Swamp who've chased the ghoul cross country since the nuclear accident turned him cannibal..."

"You call me, Tito?" asked the ghoul in a bored voice that came from a transparent breather pipe attached to the side of the pool.

Tito ignored it. "...and he started eating their relatives. And now we're supposed to be shooting the scene after the lonely widow has rescued him from the travelling aquarium. The scene where these back-woods boys arrive bent on hill-billy vengeance. Well, forget it!

We've got to emphasise the script's social commitment! We've got to show the world that our good old country is still safe from the imminent threat of bloodcrazed rubber mutants. We're going to make this movie a stirring tribute to military efficiency."

"What Mister Switch is trying to say, Smith," said Colonel Decker, snatching the megaphone from Switch's hand, turning up the volume and bel-

bullets rattled the chopper's tail, the canister hit the water, and his bikini clad discovery rose screaming into the air under the rotting grey arm of the Pool Ghoul. "Keep those screams coming, honey, do it for the folk down at the drive-ins!"

When The Face Man and Murdock had discovered that Decker was on Hannibal's tail, they'd decided it was time for some serious lawbreaking. They'd located the chopper in an empty warehouse at the naval supply depot on Terminal Island. Whilst Murdock had been starting it up, Face had looked around an adjoining warehouse for something that he might be able to use as a diversion. Feeling somewhat lost among the stacks of shark repellent, sea biscuits and inflatable rafts, he'd guessed that an anti-submarine device might do the trick.

He guessed right. Colonel Decker's rapid fire order came out, "Rapid Splutch," as the depth charge turned two tons of earth and eight hundred gallons of water into a bubbling

lowing directly down Hannibal's breather pipe, "is that you're sitting in the sights of sixty automatic rifles. You're on your own and we've got you cold. My boys start firing in five seconds. I'll count them for you in case you've got the kind of cheap watch that won't work underwater."

On the count of one, Tito Switch climbed behind one of his cameras and signalled his crew to start filming. On the count of two, to Switch's delight, Renata Ramirez began paddling down the pool and screaming in alarm. On three, Renata kept on screaming, the surface of the pool water stayed unbroken, and a whispering sound began to float up the valley toward the house. On four, sixty safety catches clicked simultaneously as the grey-skinned, bug-eyed, no-nosed, slime-covered face of the Pool Ghoul, aka Colonel Hannibal Smith, poked up into the open air. On five, as the Pool Ghoul blew a stream of water from between red plastic fangs, the whispering grew louder than Renata's screams and a US Navy chopper skimmed up over the roof of Switch's house, the rope ladder that trailed beneath it clattering across the rooftops as it came. As the ladder swung free of the roof and looped down across the tiled patio and into the water, Hannibal grabbed it in his left hand. Then he heard a burst of automatic fire behind him and saw The Face Man rolling a barrel-shaped object out of the chopper's open doorway and he grabbed hold of Renata as well.

"Beautiful, beautiful, beautiful," Tito Switch murmured into his viewfinder as tracer

avalanche of mud, metal and broken tiles with piranhas painted on. By the time that Decker and his men had dug their way out from beneath it and stared down at the quarter inch of water at the bottom of the crater that had been Tito Switch's swimming pool, the chopper was already half a mile down the valley.

"Pool Ghoul meets The Mud Men," muttered Tito B. Switch in awe as he staggered around in a daze, holding a can of film to his breast as lovingly as a mother might hold a long lost child. "Cut it, and print it."

On board the helicopter, Hannibal was asking Face what he'd found out about Micky Ling.

"B.A. tailed him from the icecream stall yesterday. Micky followed your instructions exactly. He's clean. When we picked him up at his apartment this morning he told us his old man had been having trouble with a Chinese gangster named Kwang. We were on our way to get you when B.A. made a couple of Decker's men on guard

outside Mammoth Studios. We figured you'd have trouble when they caught up with you so we paid a visit on the Navy."

"But then the whole surprise party went wrong," said Murdock, sounding like a child denied a treat, his eyes staring straight at Hannibal in blank sincerity. "I wanted marimba players and wrestling rabbits. But you think the Facial One would listen? 'Fly the chopper, Murdock!' I could have told him what was going to happen if he dropped a barrel of beer from that height, but you think the Facial One can understand hops? It's BOOM and no barbecue. No beer, no pool, no party. But who listens to Murdock?" He turned away in disgust and smiled at Renata Ramirez. She smiled back.

By the time he'd brought the chopper down on the sixteenth green of the El Dorado golf course, she'd learned that amongst the creatures who DID listen to Murdock were frogs that stayed frogs no matter how often you kissed them, certain species of invisible ant, and

some trees he'd once seen in a Clint Eastwood movie.

Hidden amongst a small stand of trees B.A. and Micky Ling were waiting for them in the A-Team truck. Micky's eyes closed as B.A. jumped the van over a sand trap. A startled golfer, abandoning thoughts of an eagle, dived for the safety of the sand, his nose landing a half inch from his ball. As they pulled up beside the chopper Micky slid open the van's side door, then stepped back in surprise as a ghoul smoking a cigar and then a brunette in a bikini climbed in. Face grabbed hold of Murdock, who was exchanging phone numbers with the helicopter, and shoved him into the van behind them. Hannibal peeled off his mask and introduced himself to Micky. As Face handed Renata a shirt and a pair of jeans and B.A. swerved between two caddy cars and out onto Willow Street, Micky continued to stare intently at Hannibal. Eventually he told him his face seemed familiar.

"The guy with the grey whiskers who sold you the icecream

yesterday is a real close relative of mine," said Hannibal with a smile. "Now tell me about Kwang."

In the A-Team's line of work it was a familiar enough story — underworld slime trying to take over things that had taken decent folk years to build. It was a chain of Chinese restaurants which Kwang needed to launder the profits from his gambling and narcotics rackets. When Mister Ling had refused to give in to Kwang's threats two of his restaurants had been bombed in the early hours of the morning. A phone call had told Mister Ling that the next bomb to go off in one of his restaurants would take some customers with it.

"Okay, Micky," said Hannibal, when Micky had finished speaking, "you just hired yourself the A-Team. We'll get the barefoot contessa a cab and then we'll go talk to your father."

They dropped Renata at a cab stand on the edge of Chinatown and gave the driver of the lead cab instructions to take her back to Tito B. Switch's home in the Hollywood Hills.

"You can't miss it," said Hannibal to the cabbie. "It's the only house without a pool."

Micky directed them through the quarter's narrow, teeming streets, past the market stalls, the pagoda-topped phone booths, and the painted dragons that decorated the arcades and bars. However, when they reached the Jade Palace, the restaurant where they had expected to meet Mister Ling, a man in a chef's apron ran out into the street and began to talk rapidly in Chinese to Micky. When he had finished speaking, Micky turned to Hannibal and told him that Kwang's men had taken his father away an hour ago to Kwang's house in the Rolling Hills behind Palos Verdes Beach.

"They'll keep him there until they force him to do what they want," said Micky bitterly. "Kwang has about twenty men up there. No one can get in or out."

"Guys," said Hannibal solemnly as he tipped a long ash from the stub of his cigar, "it looks like Mister Kwang has started himself a war. Seems like a man can't order a prawn cracker in peace any longer. Kwang thinks he's being foxy but we're going to nail him to the henhouse door."

"Just what you got in mind, Hannibal?" asked B.A. suspiciously. "You sound like you're planning one of your plans. One of your trouble plans."

"Depends which side you look at it from, B.A.," said Hannibal, smiling. "Either way, though, Kwang's bought himself a ticket in the rough house raffle."

The sign on the door of the second storey apartment said that a Mr Lee lived there. When Hannibal rang the bell a small hatch opened in the doorway and a thin face with a bald head and pointed black beard peered out at him. He asked Hannibal what he wanted. Hannibal swayed on his feet, hiccupped

and introduced himself as Wilbur Grubb of Forest Springs, Idaho.

"And this is my cousin, Hiram Grubb," he added, indicating Murdock, who stood beside him drinking from a bottle in a brown paper wrap. "Me and Hiram came here on a coach tour and just kinda got lost with all these narrow streets and bars." He giggled and hiccupped again then fumbled in his back pocket and took out a crumpled wad of bills. "We were sampling the bourbon and rice wine in a speakeasy down the street when a little guy told us we might find some action here."

The man behind the door looked at them in a measured, calculating fashion but did not speak.

"Dice," said Murdock, sticking his face up against the hatchway in the door, taking another swig from the bottle, belching, and fixing the man inside with a stare. "You savvy? Little square bones with black dots on them. Or maybe a little old fashioned American poker. We play Montana Red Dog rules back in Forest Springs, but me

and Wilbur will pick up cards in any old game you boys care to call. Can't see the odds or the opposition being tougher here than they are on Fridays down at Uncle Billy's barber shop. What you reckon, cuzz?"

"Reckon you're right, cousin," said Hannibal in a voice that oozed small town smugness. "Course, maybe these boys can't handle a couple of high rollers like the Grubbs."

The bald man, convinced now that a couple of marks had fallen into his lap, pushed back a bolt and let them in. In the centre of the room five men were playing cards at a circular table beneath a bright white bulb in a rattan shade. They looked up in idle curiosity at the two newcomers. Murdock smiled, said howdy and then threw the bottle through a plate glass mirror on the far wall of the room. The bald man's hand reach into his pocket and came up with a knife. Before he could make his move Hannibal's elbow caught him in the stomach and as he doubled up Murdock kicked the knife from his grasp. It went skidding

across the polished floorboards towards the table. One of the players leant over as if to grab it, another reached into his coat.

"Freeze, suckers!" yelled B.A., kicking in the window and training a machine gun on them from where he stood on the fire escape.

"The game's over and it looks like you gentlemen lose," said The Face Man, stepping past B.A. and starting to collect the money from around the table. "Unless you figure a knife on the floor and a handgun in the hole beats an M16."

"All right, Mister Lee," said Hannibal, grabbing the bald guy by the collar and picking him up. "You can tell your boss Kwang that he's playing with the A-Team now. Let me explain the rules. We hit one of his operations every half hour until we get Mr Ling back safe. Any money we pick up along the way will help pay Mr Ling for his damages. Now talk, and talk fast – I want to know who runs your scumbag narcotics scam and where they operate from."

"Tell him and you're a dead man, Lee," said one of the men at the table.

"You got it the wrong way round, sucker," said B.A., levelling the M16 to his shoulder. "Telling him is the only thing going to save any of your lives."

"Tell him Lee," said the man at the table, apparently undergoing a sudden change of heart.

Hannibal clapped him approvingly on the shoulder. Lee spat and remained silent.

"I've known fish more talkative than these guys," said Murdock, clambering out onto the fire escape with his hat full of half the money from the poker game. Face stepped out after him with the other half already in his wallet. "A family of sea bass to be exact. They ran a Marine Park. The marines used to wear aqualungs and watch the seahorse races. On Tuesdays you couldn't move for sharkskin suits."

"That's just Murdock's talk,"

said B.A. "Crazy man's talk. You guys better listen to a little sense."

"Sense" was a brief burst of fire from the automatic weapon that shattered the bottles and glasses on a bar at the far side of the room.

"Okay, okay," said one of the men, "there's a guy named Benson. He works out of a warehouse down at Long Beach. The warehouse is Kwang's. Benson runs the stuff from there."

"Then let's go pay Mister Benson a visit," said Hannibal, vaulting the windowledge to the fire escape.

B.A. sent the poker players ducking under the table with another burst of automatic fire and the A-Team hurried down the fire escape to their waiting panel truck.

However, they didn't head for Kwang's Long Beach Warehouse. They didn't need to. They'd already paid Benson a visit there an hour earlier.

"You figure Lee's made his call to Kwang yet?" asked Face.

"Lee will be finished by now," said Hannibal. "Right now Kwang will be wondering why he can't get a reply from Mister Benson down at his warehouse."

"Maybe he can get a reply," said Face. "Maybe Murdock forgot to lock the doors on the

container."

"Will you stop worrying which end of the rope Murdock's tied to," said Murdock in a tone that suggested he was gravely offended. "You sure you remembered to bring those sacks of Colombian death dust from the warehouse?"

"They're right here, Murdock," said Hannibal, indicating three tightly wrapped packages on the floor at his feet. "And they're going to turn Kwang into a turnip picker for the next six years. And if Micky counted Kwang's men right on their way down to the warehouse then we're going to know just how hard it's going to be to deliver Kwang's passport to prison."

Micky was waiting for them in a tangle of sea grasses and dwarf pines close to the gate of Kwang's house. He said he'd seen three cars leave, each of them carrying four or five men.

"Which leaves between seven and ten inside," said Hannibal, slotting an M70 grenade launcher into its firing tube and levelling it at a car parked at the gatehouse. There was a dull, popping sound as the weapon kicked in his hands and the empty car somersaulted backward in a ball of flame. Three men ran out from the gatehouse and as they did, Murdock and Face stepped out of the shadows beside it holding pistols and told them to lie face down on the ground. Murdock stood over them as Face ran into the gatehouse and answered the phone ringing there. Someone was speaking angrily in Chinese from the other end. Face waited for the panel truck to stop briefly in the gateway while Micky jumped down from it.

"Okay, Micky," said The Face, handing Micky the receiver. "Go frighten him some more."

As Face climbed aboard the panel truck with B.A. and Hannibal, Micky, pretending to be one of the guards, told Kwang

that there was firefight at the gate and that he needed reinforcements.

"That guy Kwang sure likes to let others do his fighting for him, don't he, Hannibal?" said B.A. as another five men burst out of the front of the house. Hannibal fired another grenade which took out the left hand pillar of the porch and its roof fell in on the men beneath it in a shower of timber and stone.

"Okay, B.A.," yelled Hannibal. "Let's go get Mister Ling!"

But they didn't need to. The five men struggling to free themselves from beneath the wreckage of the porch were the last of Kwang's bodyguards and without them his courage collapsed and he had left Mr Ling and made a run for it. B.A. found him hiding crouched in the shower, picked him up and pushed him across the room. Hannibal caught him, threw him into a chair and B.A. tied him up. As he did so the sound of approaching police sirens grew louder and Hannibal put "Kwang's" three packages of contraband narcotics onto a shelf above the sink.

"Looks like your days in the drug rackets are over, Kwang," said Hannibal. "I figured you'd be too smart to dirty your own hands with this kind of poison so I decided to do a little dirtying for you. Let's go, B.A."

Downstairs, Face and Murdock had rounded up Kwang's men and had them facing the wall. Hannibal handed Micky the grenade launcher and told him to bring the banister rail down on them if anybody moved. Mister Ling, who was standing beside his son, turned to thank Hannibal and the other members of the A-Team.

But like The Lone Ranger, the military's four most wanted men had faded into the night before they could be properly thanked. There was work to be done, thought Hannibal. With any luck, casting would start tomorrow for *Pool Ghoul III*.

FAST TRAIN TO MEDICINE BEND

The A-Team's panel truck pulled up at the Colorado roadhouse just as it was getting light. B.A. Baracus switched off the engine and sat in the driver's seat for a moment listening to the lonely country artistry of the late, great Hank Williams coming from the jukebox inside. He climbed down and flexed his stiff arms and legs as he walked over to the entrance. Inside, he pulled a chair from under a sleeping drunk, kicked over a table, and stared round at the roadhouse's clientele. From beneath the moose antlers that hung from the wall, the clientele – the remnants of last night's revellers, plus truckers and hunters having a breakfast beer for the road – stared back at him.

"This Judge Hansen's establishment?" asked B.A.

"That's right, boy," said the barman, reaching down under the counter with his left hand. "What you lookin' for?"

"I'm looking for prompt service, sucker," said B.A., smashing the chair to matchwood across the man's shoulder. "I'm looking for a glass of cold milk and I'm looking for it fast."

A long night spent on the interstates had done nothing for B.A.'s attitude. As Hank Williams continued to sing mournfully on the jukebox, B.A.'s frown turned into a scowl. He picked up a bottle from the top of the bar and flung it through the jukebox's glass dome. Hank Williams' voice slid down about six octaves as it ground to a halt.

"That sucker complains too much," he muttered to himself as he picked a little guy off a bar stool and hung him up from the antlers of an elk.

"Now just hold on there, boy," said a man grabbing hold of B.A.'s shoulder from behind. "Just who do you think..." His voice stopped suddenly as B.A.'s

elbow hit him between the eyes. As the man went down, his partner, who was wearing a red baseball hat, took a swing at B.A.

B.A. caught the man's fist in his left hand and then pulled the man's cap down over his face with his right. It was a move he'd learned from trying to shut Murdock up when he started his crazy talk. The four sharp jabs to the front of the cap that followed, however, were pure wish fulfilment. Somehow the crazy man had always been too slippery to stand still for these, he thought, as a chair smashed down on top of his head. He turned to kick the feet out from under an open-mouthed man holding a single broken chair leg. B.A. felt the aggressions that a night on the road had conjured up beginning to fade into a more relaxed mood as he punched out the barman's assistant, and, as he flung a fat-jowelled, crew cut figure in a checked shirt through a flimsy wooden screen into a stack of beer crates, he wondered how much longer he was going to have to wait before that sucker sheriff from Medicine Bend showed up.

As the train turned northward through Raton, Trinidad and Pueblo, Linda Shepherd watched the telegraph poles flick past the window as quickly as the pages of a comic book, and wondered whether she was going crazy. On the rack above her head was a briefcase which contained torn up sheets of newspaper. She had been given it by an old man selling bait on the Santa Monica Pier the previous day. She had given him a bag containing twenty thousand dollars in return. It had been money their father had left to put her younger brother Bobby through medical school. But Bobby was locked up in a prison in Medicine Bend, and the sheriff, the judge, and the prison governor who had put him there wanted twenty thousand dollars to let him go.

On the seat opposite her a bespectacled young man was reading the *Wall Street Journal*. On the seat next to her an ointment salesman from Boothsburg, Idaho was trying to impress her with the purity of his product. He had opened the sample case on his lap and was holding up a small brown bottle for her inspection.

"Tarkington's Ocean Lotion," he announced proudly. "Brewed, stewed, and blended in Boothsburg, Idaho, from a recipe learned from the pearl divers of the Andaman Islands. All natural products. You ever heard of kelp? Soft coral? The Portuguese man o' war? Salt water mangos? They're all here in Tarkington's Ocean Lotion, helping to keep the flower of the nation's manhood free from pimples."

Linda smiled politely at the drummer. She'd thought that time and big business had driven such characters out of exis-

tence; that, like the Great Train Robbery, Indian attacks and the iron horse, they had become part of railroad legend. If they had, though, someone had forgotten to tell Aloysius Tarkington of Boothsburg, Idaho, and Linda, too polite to tell him she wasn't interested, pretended to listen to his sales pitch whilst her mind ran back across the events that had brought her there.

First there had been the phone call from Bobby saying he'd been arrested in a little Colorado town called Medicine Bend whilst he had been hitch hiking through. Although he had sounded nervous he told her not to worry, that it was all a mistake. The next call had come from the sheriff of Medicine Bend who had said Bobby had been found guilty of unlawful possession of narcotics and was going to have to spend five years on the Medicine Bend Prison Farm unless she brought up the twenty thousand dollars Bobby

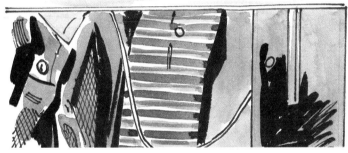

said he had put by to see him through school.

"And listen, honey," the voice had said with a flat, friendly chuckle, "there ain't no use your talking to police. After all, you're talking to them right now."

It was then that she'd decided to try and find the A-Team but, like most people who went looking for them, she met two days of dead ends, broken appointments and bamboozles while they checked her out. Then two nights ago she had found a note slipped into her bag which had told her to go to The Texas Rose Country Cabaret Lounge. She'd watched Charlene Henderson and her Country Critters – a pedal steel player, an upright bass, a break dancer, and four toy poodles – play to a large and noisy house until a waitress in a white stetson had given her a message to take the next bus north along Branding Iron Boulevard. Outside, she'd col-

lided with a passing priest as she ran for the bus, and as she saw it pull away from the kerb and he helped her to her feet, she'd found herself tearfully telling him her whole story.

Next day, she'd found an empty brown briefcase on the doorstep of her apartment and a note inside it had told her to put the twenty thousand dollars in it and go down to the fishing pier at Santa Monica.

At the fishing pier the bait-seller had switched cases and told her the A-Team would get in touch. They had done so as soon as she got home. A man who said his name was Smith had phoned and told her to take the bag that the bait-seller had given her and take the next train for Medicine Bend. The line went dead before she could even ask why.

Linda's train of thought was interrupted by a persistent prodding at her elbow. She looked up to see Mister Tarkington holding out a small card.

"I think he's trying to show you his business card," said the man with the spectacles, flashing her a look of sympathy as he folded his newspaper and got to his feet.

Linda took the drummer's card and read it. It said: LAST TIME WE MET I WAS SELLING BAIT. THE GUYS IN THE CORNER SEAT HAVE BEEN TAILING YOU FOR THE PAST FORTY-EIGHT HOURS. TAKE YOUR CASE AND GO TO CABIN 17 AT THE REAR OF THE TRAIN. DON'T BE SCARED. WE'LL GET YOUR BROTHER BACK. HANNIBAL SMITH. When she looked up again, Mister Aloysius Tarkington of Boothsburg, Idaho was still staring the same bland, salesman's smile at her.

Linda stood up, took her bag down from the rack and walked past the two men in the corner

seat. When she reached cabin seventeen she looked back and saw the two men coming down the corridor towards her. Behind them, holding his brown derby on his head with one hand, a caseful of Tarkington's Ocean Lotion samples in the other, was Hannibal.

She knocked on the door and it opened immediately. To her surprise she found the bespectacled young man who had been reading the *Wall Street Journal* beckoning her silently inside. As soon as she was inside he pushed her through the open connecting door into the next compartment. There was a knock on the door that opened onto the corridor and the man opened it and asked the two men standing there what they wanted. At that moment Hannibal appeared behind them and shoved them both forward into the compartment. The bespectacled man stepped out of the way and let them fall and then stepped through the door into the adjoining compartment and locked it. The two men were still lying in a heap beneath the sleeping berths when Hannibal threw a bottle of Tarkington's Ocean Lotion to the floor. As soon as it shattered, the cabin began to fill with a thick grey gas. One of them put his hands to his eyes and began to crawl towards the doorway.

"Not this time, pal," said Hannibal, slamming the door on his nose and hanging a Do Not Disturb sign on the doorhandle. "You two buzzards have booked a sleeper. All the way to Chicago."

"Who were those guys?" asked Linda as she and Face stepped out of cabin sixteen.

"They must be working for the same people who've got Bobby. They were waiting for you to get hold of the twenty grand and then they were going to rip it off. That's why I changed bags," explained Hannibal.

"Here's your money, Linda," said Face, handing her a brown briefcase. He opened it to show her her twenty thousand dollars, paused and let his glance linger on the bills inside, then sighed and snapped it shut.

"We checked out your story, Linda," said Hannibal. "It seems the citizens of Medicine Bend are short on hospitality. Their sheriff and their judge in particular have been making a habit of picking up vagrants and drifters – people without any clout to fight them – and they've been framing them and putting them to work on the prison farms and factories. There's fat profits to be made if you pay your workforce two dollars a week." He took a cigar from his pocket, looked at his watch, then looked out the train window. About a half mile further up the track a line of cars were waiting at a crossing barrier for the train to pass. Hannibal reached up and pulled down the communication cord. As the train slowed down with a series of shuddering bumps that sent passengers spilling from their seats, Hannibal opened the train door. He told Linda to get off at the next station, hire a car and drive straight back to L.A. Then he jumped.

"We've got to help stop a riot," explained The Face as he jumped after him.

The sheriff of Medicine Bend arrested B.A. at 7.30 am. By 9.30 the judge, a late riser, had sentenced him to a seven year stretch in the Medicine Bend Penitentiary. At 10.30 the prison gates closed behind him. By noon he had fused the prison's electrical system, started a riot in the dining hall, disarmed a guard in the confusion, and was now headed for the governor's office with Bobby Shepherd.

He peered round the corner of a corridor and saw two guards standing nervously at the governor's door. He gave Bobby his

gun and then told Bobby to march him towards them. B.A. walked in front of him with his hands in the air. When he had got close enough he knocked their heads together, took their weapons away and then kicked down the door. The prison governor was reaching into a drawer in his desk. B.A. reached over and slammed the drawer shut on his hand. Then he put the automatic weapon to the side of his head.

"Alright, sucker," he said, "this is what you do. You get the phone and you call your friends the judge and the sheriff. You tell them that if they don't get over here and sign this boy's release papers then their whole dirty racket's going straight to the federal police. You got that?" The governor, who had turned paler than a kid full of candy floss on a roller coaster, nodded and picked up the phone. "And when you've done that, sucker, you unlock your safe," growled B.A. "I want my

gold back."

Murdock had been waiting for Hannibal and Face in a grey sedan. Without a word he spun the car round and headed away from the railroad track as soon as they were both inside it. Hannibal peeled off his bald wig and grey whiskers as they drove, and then changed into a grey suit. He'd just put on a pair of reflector glasses and a thin moustache when they arrived at the prison gates.

"Name's McGuire. Head of the state's hostage negotiation team," he said, flashing his credentials at the guards on the gate. "Give me an update."

The guard looked at his credentials then called up to a man in a lookout tower to ask who'd sent for the state hostage negotiation team.

"The governor did," snapped Hannibal. "Now tell me what's happening before someone gets killed."

"There's two of them. They've got Judge Hansen and Sheriff

Sloan as well as the governor. They say if we move against them they'll kill them."

"That's what they all say," said Hannibal, jamming a cigar into his mouth. "Now just open the gates and let me and my boys get to work."

When the gates opened, Murdock raced the car across the empty prison yard to the building that contained the governor's office. He skidded to a halt outside the door and Hannibal and Face sprinted for it. When the door closed behind them Murdock looked up at the row of rifles and automatics trained down on him from the prison walls and he raised his finger to his lips, hunched his shoulders, and gave them a knowing, secretive wink.

Five minutes later Hannibal appeared at the doorway. "Hold your fire and open the gates!" he yelled across the yard. "We're coming out."

Moments later Sloan, Hansen, and the governor hurried head down toward the rear of the car. Then B.A. and Bobby Shepherd were marched out in handcuffs by The Face Man. They got in the front beside Murdock. Hannibal, holding an automatic weapon, climbed on the front fender of the car, while Face climbed on the rear fender.

"Hurry up and drive, fool," said B.A. through gritted teeth as he counted the guns pointing down at him.

"Be nice to Murdock," said Murdock, "otherwise he might tell these state troopers that the Baracan One has been a bad boy."

"I'm going to break your fool head, Murdock."

"Not now you're not, B.A.," said Hannibal, without looking down from the row of guns. "Take this taxi home, Murdock."

The overloaded sedan moved slowly across the yard to the gateway, the guns on the wall following it as it went. At the gate a guard stepped out and flagged them down. Murdock halted once again. The guard looked in through the window and nodded respectfully to the governor, judge, and sheriff. They nodded back at him without speaking.

"We've been on to the state capital, trying to get through to your department to get the necessary clearance you're going to need to take out these two prisoners with you, but we can't get through to them."

"That's because they don't exist, friend," said Hannibal with a relaxed smile as he detonated the charges he had left primed in the governor's office.

As the side of the building blew out in a chaos of bricks and flaming timber the trooper turned his head just long enough for Hannibal to deck him with a left cross. Murdock had them through the gates before he'd hit the ground, and Face kept the marksmen on the wall down with a spray of automatic fire.

"What we gonna do with these three?" asked Murdock as they bounced down the dirt road away from the prison. "Lock them up with a bathtub full of baby snakes? Let the Baracan One massage their faces with those big knuckles of his? Make them drink soda pop till they burst?"

"Hope," said Hannibal as Murdock wheeled the car along the side of a ravine. Hannibal had a pair of field glasses to his eyes and he pointed down the track to an approaching column of armoured cars. "We're going to leave them for the REAL riot police."

Murdock stopped the car and Face Man and B.A. handcuffed the crooked lawmen to the front bumper. Hannibal took the prison records he had taken from the prison governor's safe and scattered them over the seats of the car. He figured enough there to put them away for fifteen or twenty years.

"If that's the riot police in front," said Murdock, scratching his head and pointing to the approaching armoured cars, "and that's the riot behind..." He pointed back up the trail toward the prison. "How are we gonna get out from between them?"

"We swim," said Hannibal, pointing at the river fifty feet below them at the bottom of the ravine.

"But Murdock doesn't like swimming," said Murdock.

"Stop your whining, fool. It sure beats flying," said B.A., giving him a shove.

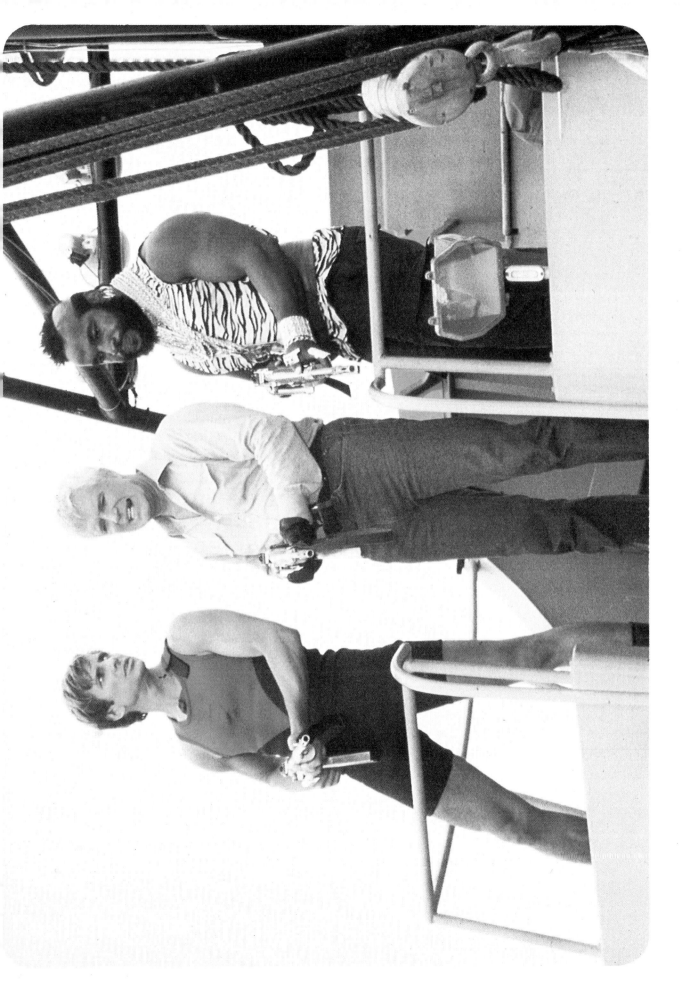

SP-LUSH!

AS POWERFUL CURRENTS DRAG THE STRICKEN 301 UNDER...

...POWERFUL HANDS COME TO THE A-TEAM'S RESCUE.

SPLUTTER! WHAT HAPPENED? WHERE ARE WE?

IT DON'T LOOK LIKE HEAVEN.

THAT NIGHT...

ARE THEY MAKING ANY SENSE TO YOU, FACE?

SURE. THEY DON'T LIKE MANANGA EITHER. LAST WEEK HE KIDNAPPED SIX OF THEIR MEN AS SLAVES.

THAT'S RIGHT. THEY WANT REVENGE!

WELL, BOYS, AFTER SAVING OUR LIVES, THE LEAST WE CAN DO IS HELP THEM GET IT! HERE'S THE PLAN...

DAWN COMES EARLY IN THE TROPICS...

AS THE NATIVES MOUNT A DIVERSIONARY ATTACK...

UGH? WHAT THE— INDIANS!

TARZAN OF THE
FARMYARD

J.J. McPherson pulled down his straw hat to shade his grizzled face from the hot Arizona sun and quietly sucked his home made pipe as he watched the red, blue and black panel truck approaching his ranch. When it came to a halt in a flurry of dust he uncrossed his long bony legs, climbed slowly out of his rocking chair, and stepped forward to greet the A-Team.

"Of course, I ain't got a lot of money," he said, after the introductions had been made, "and those company boys could offer you a whole lot of dollars –"

"Your son is a buddy of ours," Hannibal interrupted. "He's good people."

"Right!" affirmed B.A. roughly. "He is a brother. And we don't sell our brothers for no C note salad."

J.J. nodded slowly, looked them over carefully with his tired, sun rinsed eyes, then led them inside.

J.J. McPherson was a rancher who had struggled for years to build up a small herd of high quality cattle on his ranch. His wife had died young and the only help he'd had was that of his son, P.J., who'd served in South East Asia with Hannibal. Things had been beginning to look good until someone started senselessly butchering his stock. In the late night chase

after the culprits, P.J.'s pick-up had taken a .357 mm slug in the front off tyre, flipped over the jettisoned carcass of a pure bred Guernsey cow, and plunged two hundred feet down a sheer cliff face. The doctors said it was even money whether he would see another sunrise.

"And you're sure it's the oil company trying to put you out of business?" asked Hannibal, pulling on a beer can in the cool of the kitchen.

J.J. nodded. "Reckon so."

"Have you got any proof?" asked Face Man.

"Nope. Just a feeling."

Hannibal finished his beer and expertly flipped the empty

can into the waste basket. "That will do for us, J.J.," he said. "From now on, you're working with the A-Team."

An hour later, Hannibal, Face, Murdock and B.A. were being given a guided tour of J.J.'s spread. As they stood by a handful of peacefully grazing Ayrshire calves, J.J. prodded the ground with a walking stick.

"P.J. had some tests done last year," he explained. "The company said there was no oil there, but soon after – the trouble starts."

"What do you think, B.A.?" asked Hannibal.

"I think we should find these dudes and beat them to a jelly."

"Not strawberry flavoured," warned Murdock. "That can be dangerous. It's so green and–"

He was cut off by an eerily familiar whistle that grew louder and louder. Hannibal and B.A.'s eyes locked in recognition and Face pushed J.J. to the floor.

"Incoming!" yelled B.A., diving for the floor. "Eat dirt!"

The mortar shell slammed into the ground twenty yards from where they stood, pounding inside their ears like red hot hammers, sand-blasting their bodies with grit and dirt, and sending twisted lumps of smoking red hot metal whistling inches over their heads. The calves panicked wildly, bellow-

ing noisily and running for their lives as the mortar on the hill 'walked' its deadly payload after them. The A-Team scrambled to its feet and sprinted to the panel truck. Murdock took the wheel as the others piled in.

"They're going to pay for this," he snarled. "They're going to be sorry they ever set foot in my domain."

"This land is J.J.'s, you crazy fool!" B.A. pointed out.

"That may be so on paper," said Murdock, spinning the wheel so the tyres locked in a half turn, then letting them free as the truck sped off to the hillside where the shells had come from. "But everyone knows that from the grassy plains of the North Forty to the small pig pen on Mrs O'Rafferty's dirt shack, the real ruler of all he surveys, the rightful Prince of Poultry, the Dashing Duke of Domestic Livestock, the Monarch of Milk, Baron of Barns, Chancellor of Chickenhood – the only heir to the Eggy Empire, is me – Tarzan of the Farmyard!"

B.A. leaned forward and grabbed Murdock's neck in a vice-like grip.

"No, B.A. – stop!" pleaded Face, trying to dislodge B.A.'s arm. "He's driving!"

"Crazy fool sounds like he's flying! An' if you don't let go my arm I'm gonna–"

"Now hold on a minute," drawled Hannibal from the back. "I know you're riled up, B.A. – but you can't strangle Murdock because he's driving and you can't stomp Face because we're gonna need his lucky face." B.A. reluctantly released his grip on Murdock's neck and pushed his face close to Hannibal's. He looked like lightning waiting for somewhere to strike. "Er... and you can't work out on me," Hannibal explained, "because I'm the only one with a plan."

B.A.'s frown intensified as the bouncing truck screeched round the corner of a narrow dirt road that led to the top of

the hill. On one side was steep drop guarded by a flimsy wood and wire fence, on the other the slope was covered with loose rocks, rough shale and dry brown bushes. Murdock let out a lung-bursting cockerel's cry and was flapping his elbows when another incoming round hit a pile of boulders up ahead and started a small avalanche tumbling down the slope into the path of the speeding van.

Murdock swerved to the left, ploughing down the makeshift fence, the outer wheels of the van barely gripping the rough uneven road. He gunned the motor with his foot to the floor, and at the moment a victorious *cock-a-doodle-doo!* was forming on his lips, a massive lumbering rock sideswiped the rear of the van, and as it raced, teetering along the edge, Murdock fell out over the cliff.

Face leaned one way to pull on the wheel as the others leaned the other to try and balance the truck. Face pulled, and as the truck screeched back onto the road, he slipped behind the wheel and slammed on the brakes. The A-Team vehicle screamed up the slope on the other side of the road, came churning to a halt, then gently flipped over onto its side. Hannibal was first out with a belt of grenades and and Armalite rifle with a rocket launcher mounted underneath. Face and B.A. followed, with B.A. carrying a heavy 14.5 mm KPV machine gun and Face with an Uzi in each hand. Hannibal's face was grim. "Spread out, boys," he said, shielding his eyes from the sun as he looked up at the top of the hill, trying to pinpoint the mortar's exact position. "We're going to teach those murdering scumbags how to play 'King of the Hill'!"

But even as they opened up they could see it was too late. The insistent chatter of a Kawasaki KH-4 was followed by the sight of the insect-like chopper rising from the top of the hill, banking sharply and

swinging back out of their line of fire. B.A. stamped his feet on the ground, Face shook his head wearily and Hannibal's usual smile was missing when he made his way to the edge of the cliff to see what had happened to Murdock. But as he was stepping over the remains of the wire fence to look over the edge he was met by the full throated bellow of a bull Ayrshire. He leaned forward to see Murdock, thirty feet below him, swinging on one of the slats of the dislodged wire fence.

"Tarzan – you made it," said Hannibal with a smile.

"How could you ever have doubted it?" Murdock ranted, using the slats as a ladder to haul himself up with. "Me – who as a baby was the only survivor of the firt space ship to land on the planet. To someone who survived the rigours of one whole winter before being found and adopted by a friendly she-turkey – man, it was a piece of cake."

"Is that sucker still spoutin' that crazy jive?" asked B.A.,

taking his place by Hannibal's side at the cliff edge and glaring down at the veteran flier climbing up towards them. "If he'd been in the jungle, the apes would have taken a walk!"

"I didn't say I was in the jungle, B.A.," explained Murdock, pulling himself over the rim of the cliff. "You're looking at Lord Greymatter himself, big red cheese of the chicken coop. With my faithful egg Cheetah by my side, I swing from blade of grass to blade of grass, at one with mighty mother nature, the sight of my red and blue cape bringing reassurance and comfort to all my subjects."

"Tarzan didn't wear a red and blue cape," said Face, joining them. "And though it might seem a little pernickety to point it out – neither do you."

"Tarzan of the chicken coop's cape is invisible, Face," said Murdock, indignantly. "Every-

body knows that."

"Everybody knows you ain't playin' with a full deck," said B.A., clenching his fists.

Hannibal stepped between him and Murdock. "I got three words to say to the whole bunch of you," he smiled. "Stop arguing."

"That's two words, Hannibal," B.A. growled.

"You see, you've started again already. Now let's get this truck back on the road. Tomorrow, we storm the Bastille."

The following morning, oil company president Willie Bob Anderson was studying the latest stock exchange figures as his car radio went through the usual litany of violence, greed, deception and corruption that makes up the news. As usual, he travelled alone in the back of his Rolls Royce Silver Shadow with only his chauffeur for company. Four of his bodyguards

travelled in the black Cadillac immediately ahead of him and four more in the identical car immediately behind. If Willie Bob hadn't been so interested in his figures, and if his chauffeur hadn't been impatiently staring at the lights, waiting for them to change, maybe one of them would have noticed that in the car behind, the four bodyguards were gaping slack-jawed with fear down the barrel of a Thompson machine gun which Face, astride a 1000 cc Harley Davidson, was pointing at them while Murdock, clucking happily to himself, taped grenades to the windows of their car, carefully wiring the pins so that if the doors were opened, the grenades would go off.

In fact, the first inkling that Willie Bob and chauffeur had that something weird was going down was when a huge fist, covered in rings, came crashing through the window and a thick muscular arm reached inside and ripped the radio from its casing and crushed it in front of their eyes.

"That is the end of the news, suckers!" said an extremely gruff voice as the arm dropped the radio, opened the door from the inside and dragged out the chauffeur. The chauffeur was trying to clear his gun from his highly polished holster when B.A., still sitting on his powerful Harley, put him down briskly with a right uppercut.

"Nice work, B.A.," called Hannibal from his motorcycle on the other side of the Rolls. "But I think the monkeys in the cage ahead are getting restless." Hannibal nodded towards the lead car, where one of the bodyguards was stepping out with a Heckler and Koch machine pistol in his hands.

"You suckers just don't learn!" said B.A., climbing off his bike, lifting the chrome-plated monster above his head and hurling it with both hands. It knocked the bodyguard over

and slammed into the back window of the Caddy. The tank smashed open and the remaining bodyguards jumped out in a state of panic, tearing off their petrol soaked clothes before anything could ignite them.

B.A. slid behind the wheel of the Rolls, Hannibal slipped in the back beside Willie Bob, and with Murdock and Face as outriders, they roared off through town into the desert, leaving behind a ransom note and eight scared bodyguards.

Later that afternoon, in a cave overlooking an abandoned trailer, Murdock, with a chicken on his shoulder and a small piglet on a lead, was demanding to know why Willie Bob had violated the code of the farmyard.

"I never knew about any of this until you told me," said Willie Bob. "I'm just a figurehead these days. Frank Bodak does most of the work."

"Do you trust this guy Bodak?" asked Hannibal.

"Of course. He was my father's right hand man until the crash."

"Crash?"

"My father was killed in a plane crash three years ago. Frank would have been with him if his wife hadn't been ill."

"And if we proved to you that Frank Bodak is a lying, murdering tub of lard with a moral sense somewhere between Vlad the Impaler and an electric toaster — you'd be willing to open your books to the law and let the cops finger him?"

"Well, yes, but —"

"But nothing," Hannibal interrupted, looking at his watch. "In the note we left we said the money had to be brought to the trailer by one man only or you'd never be seen again."

"I'm sure Frank has my safety uppermost in his mind."

"We'll soon find out," said Murdock, who had been kneeling by the piglet and squeaking noisily. "Because Simba here says they're on their way."

They watched in silence as a large white van made its way down the valley towards the trailer. It came to a halt and

after a few seconds one man got out and looked nervously around. He was carrying a large black bag.

"You see," said Willie Bob triumphantly. "That's Frank! He's followed your instructions to the letter."

"Oh yeah?" asked Hannibal as Bob put his hand inside the bag and pulled out an air-cooled MG34 7.92 mm machine gun. He barked a command and the back doors of the van flew open and seven heavily armed men piled out, took up positions and opened fire. Thousands and thousands of high velocity slugs tore through the trailer as it shuddered on its tyreless wheels, and for good measure two grenades were lobbed through the shattered windows, blowing out the door and blasting a huge hole in the floor. To round off the attack, Bodak himself took a flame thrower and played it on the wreckage until it was blazing.

"You see any bodies yet?"

Bodak asked the nearest man. The man shook his head. "Reckon the grenades probably wiped them out."

As they stood in line and admired their handiwork, Murdock and Face were quietly climbing out of the foxholes they had dug and then covered with blankets and sand. Face waved up to the cave and the two men crept carefully up behind the thugs.

"Looking for something, suckers?" growled B.A. As the hoodlums spun around he and Face sprayed two short bursts inches from their feet.

"You better drop them, boys," said Face, smiling as he levelled his weapon. "We've never missed twice."

"You can't get us all," said Frank Bodak, holding onto the flame thrower. "We're bound to get you both in the end. It's a Mexican stand-off."

"Wrong again, meatball," said Hannibal from behind him, reinforcing his words with a long burst of fire into the air. "This is no stand-off. It was supposed to be a pay-off."

"I got the money with me," Frank called over his shoulder. "Why not take it and go?"

"We'll take it, all right," Hannibal continued, "and with Willie Bob's blessing. He's mighty pleased to be rid of verminous garbage like you. The pay-off I'm talking about is when you and your plastic cowboys start day one of a long, long stretch in the slammer. Now throw down your weapons and climb in that truck."

Bodak's fingers were tensing round the flame thrower when a sudden burst from B.A. knocked it from his hands. "You heard the man, sucker. Move it!" he ordered.

And after seeing the look in his eyes, they all obeyed.

Later, as they celebrated Bodak's arrest and the news that P.J. had been removed from the critical list, Face Man asked J.J. what he planned to do.

"Don't know, really," said J.J. "Now that we know there's oil on this land I could retire, but me an' P.J. kinda like working with animals."

"Talking of animals," said B.A. "Where's that fool with the marshmallow head?"

"Murdock?" answered Hannibal. "He's flown the coop."

"You said it, Jack," muttered B.A.

"I think he said something about going outside for a while," Face explained. "Something about hypnotising a horse. He seemd to think..."

Face Man was interrupted by a loud whinnying sound and Murdock appeared at the door on all fours, pawing the floor with his hand and shaking his neck wildly from side to side. He trotted round the room and reared up in the corner. "Hey, buddies," he asked, "do any of you know how to get a horse to snap his fingers?"

SOME KIND OF DOUBLECROSS

When Colonel Decker and his men raided Emil's – an exclusive Manhattan Beach restaurant noted for the informality of its ambience – its clientele of old movie people, tennis players, successful poets and the latest young turks from the commodities market, did what anyone might do if they suddenly found the business end of an M16 pointed somewhere between their heart and their hors d'oeuvre. They panicked. Silently. Then a waiter shoved open the kitchen doors with a couple of dressed lobsters on a tray and backed into a nervous young rookie who spun around in alarm and let off an accidental burst that brought down a shelf of tropical plants on the heads of the diners sitting under them; and the once elegant informality of the place disintegrated into a chaos of shrieks, shouts, and breaking crockery.

Across the street, outside the cordon the military had thrown around the restaurant, a stooped, grey-haired man in tiny round glasses, a cardigan and bedroom slippers carefully unlocked the door of his watchmaker's shop and asked one of the soldiers facing away from the restaurant what all the fuss was about.

"Army business, old man," said the soldier impatiently as he tried to hurry the curious, dawdling spectators away. "We got a bunch of army deserters in there and they might be armed and dangerous. So move along now."

"Move along there. Do this. Do that. You think anyone has time to say please any more?" complained the old man. "Everybody's in a hurry, everybody's crazy. Your brave young captain thinks perhaps these bad men are hiding under that gentleman's wig?"

The soldier turned to see his colonel prodding tentatively at the ample belly of a bald man smoking a cigar. With as much dignity as he could muster in the situation, the man reached out, took back his wig from Colonel Decker and replaced it on his head.

"You don't know these dudes like the colonel does, grandpa," said the soldier, suppressing a smile. "They're sharp and they're slippery and they..."

"So sharp and slippery you have to fill the streets with soldiers?" the old man asked, throwing his arms up in disgust. "What a world today! For forty years now I repair watches for people. Now, a battery runs down and they throw the watch away. But what does an old man know, soldier?"

The old man turned away and shuffled toward the end of the block, still muttering irascibly to himself as he went.

On the other side of the street, a young man in phone company overalls stepped out of the payphone he had been repairing and fell into step alongside the old man. At the end of the block he crossed with the lights. "Looks like Little Miss Devonshire has sold us out, Hannibal," said the younger man as they turned the corner together.

"Maybe, Face Man, maybe," said the older, fishing a cigar from the pocket of his cardigan and straightening his stoop as they crossed the road to where B.A. and Murdock were waiting for them behind a piece of corrugated fencing they'd brought with them in the panel truck and stretched across the end of a small side entrance. "I had her figured for a real stand-up kid but it wouldn't be the first time that I've been wrong. Let's go, B.A."

"Where to, Hannibal?" asked the baddest attitude ever to go over the stockade wall.

"Kathy's place," said Hannibal as B.A. began to back down to the other end of the alleyway. As he did so an MP's jeep appeared silhouetted at its end. B.A. braked and then put the engine into first gear before the van had skidded to a halt.

"Will things be like this at Kathy's?" asked Murdock in the tone of voice he always used when the little green men had taken him for breakfast on Pluto.

"Will what be the same, sucker?" said B.A., smashing through the corrugated iron fence, shooting across the flow of oncoming traffic and skid-ding into the lane headed northward.

"Oh, you know. The sky. The earth," said Murdock dreamily, as B.A. sent the truck into a four-wheel drift that sent them across a filling station forecourt to avoid an MP's jeep and a police road block that had closed off the far side of an intersection. "You ever notice that? How well the two of them fit together? The sky joins up to the ground in a near enough perfect match. Course, I suppose if there was a gap they'd get crazy people trying to sneak inside through it."

"If you don't shut your fool mouth, Murdock, you're going to get my fist sneaking into it. Then I'm gonna pull your head off."

"Take it easy, B.A.," said Hannibal, putting a match to his cigar. "Just lose these clowns behind before you pull his head off. Then – if he's still acting crazy – you can pull his head off."

Hannibal flipped the match out of the window. Murdock threw Hannibal a look of silent hurt and then looked at B.A. As B.A. accelerated up the ramp to a level crossing and sent the A-Team's truck leaping across the flatcars of a passing freight his scowling features broke into a smile of anticipation.

The A-Team had first heard of Kathy Devonshire two days ago – a couple of hours after she had first started looking for them – and they'd run their usual routines to find out how hard she wanted to find them. The Face Man had phoned her home number and sent her round the city chasing phone calls. The last one had been to the pay phone in the lobby of a Lakewood rollerskating rink and he had told her to go down to the drinking fountain in Paradise Park and wait for somebody. Whilst she had been following the Face Man's phone calls and B.A. had been following her, Hannibal had checked her out and discovered that she was twenty-two, single, worked in the city building department, and that everybody who knew her seemed to like her.

Then, after donning a bald

wig, a Hawaiian shirt, and a moustache he picked at random, he had borrowed a hot dog stand from a guy who owed him fifty dollars from a poker game they'd got involved in when they'd been extras on the same Z movie and he'd gone down to Paradise Park to wait for her.

He'd waited until she approached him and asked if he'd seen anyone hanging around. He'd shaken his head and then he'd asked her what she wanted with the A-Team. Before she could reply there had been a crackle of static from the hidden two way and B.A.'s voice had come up through the onions to tell them that the cops were coming down on them fast.

"You call the cavalry in on us, sister?" Hannibal had asked, glancing sharply at Kathy Devonshire as B.A. stopped to let them through the side door of the van and then slotted them through the gaps in the traffic until the sound of the police

sirens was inaudible behind them. "Who are you working for?"

Hannibal remembered how the girl had faced up to his stare as she had told him that she wasn't working for anyone, and he remembered the look of surprise on her face when he had asked B.A. if she'd had anyone tailing her and B.A. had said he'd thought that he'd made two dudes in a tan sedan but he couldn't be sure.

Hannibal had decided to give the can of worms another shake and see how things were wriggling. He'd dropped Kathy three blocks from home and told her to meet him the following day in the old watchmaker's shop that had closed down across the road from Emil's, and then, if everything went sweetly, maybe they could talk.

"Take these," Kathy had said and handed him some papers as she stepped out of the truck. "They're copies of papers I took

from Mister Grove and Mister Piggot. They're why I wanted to hire the A-Team. I'll keep the originals myself until I know whether or not I can trust you guys."

"Whether YOU can trust US?" Face Man had said. "You sure you're rattling the right cage?"

"Is there any reason you shouldn't trust me?" Kathy had asked as she'd turned to walk away.

"I'm just wondering where a secretary in the housing department gets enough large denomination notes to hire the A-Team," Face had said in a level voice, and for the first time Kathy seemed uncertain in her replies.

"I... I... I don't," she had stammered. "I... I needed someone's help."

If it had been an act then it had been a good one, remembered Hannibal. If he'd needed any more convincing, he'd got it from the papers that she'd left with him. They contained details of an 'Investors' Penthouse' set up – one of the oldest property scams in the business. It went like this: first you buy a couple of prime site city blocks at bargain basement rates. Then you put up a block of luxury apartments, first raising the cash by promising private investors who invested more than ten grand free use of one of the private penthouse suites on the roof whenever they booked it. A private penthouse! Free! For life! Plus a small share in a downtown real estate investment. If you could convince a hundred people in a city of seven million then you had a million dollars. Two hundred meant two million dollars. When the building was up, you sold all of the dwelling units, penthouse suites as well. Being the prime site real estate, your profits turn out to be fat, fat, fat. Then, when they're all sold you contact your investors and tell them the penthouse scheme has run into legal difficulties and has fallen through. You return them their money like any honest man would do in the circumstances, maybe even give them a little extra for good faith. Anything left over – say a million dollars or so – you keep. It was old, sweet, and simple. And all it needed were friends like Piggot and Grove at city hall to make it work. Friend Grove to rewrite business zoning boundaries and health, fire and safety regulations, friend Piggot to buy up properties under the city's compulsory purchase laws when the cost of alterations drove them into disrepair.

Hannibal's train of thought was interrupted as B.A. pulled up in the driveway to Kathy Devonshire's house. He told B.A. and Murdock to watch the street and he and Face climbed the flight of wooden steps to Kathy's ground floor apartment. Behind them, B.A.'s irritable gaze flickered between the empty street and Murdock, who was doing his standing - around - with - his - hands - in - his - pockets - whistling - and - looking - normal routine. B.A. wasn't fooled for a second and told him to stop acting crazy unless he wanted to feel his fist on his fool head.

There was no reply to Hannibal's knock on the apartment door. Face let Hannibal knock a second time then flexed his fingers, took out a pin and a credit card and worked his street-magic on the locks. He pushed the door tentatively ajar with his fingertips and it opened to reveal an empty room.

"See, Hannibal," said The Face. "The lady turns us then splits."

"I don't think so, Face Man," said Hannibal. "If she was trying to turn us then why did she send Decker's men across the street to Emil's?"

"Maybe it was all she could remember," said Face Man.

"And maybe you got her figured all wrong," said Hannibal, noticing where the lock on a

mahogany bureau had been forced, and indicating the kitchen, bedroom, and bathroom, where the contents of cupboards and drawers had been spilled across the floor. "Somebody's knocked this place over."

"We got trouble, Hannibal," said Murdock, sticking his head round the door. "Decker again."

Hannibal and Face stepped onto the porch and then jumped down into the back of the A-Team's panel truck which B.A. had backed up across the lawn. Murdock lobbed a couple of smoke grenades into the path of Decker's approaching jeeps then jumped in. From out of the smoke came the sounds of screeching tyres and the crunch of colliding vehicles as B.A. made it to the end of the block and made a right.

"Face it, Hannibal," said The Face Man as B.A. sideswiped a jeep that swerved across in front of them to try and block their path. "She's served us up to Decker with everything but an apple in our mouths."

"Not necessarily," said Murdock, holding up a finger like a defending council in an afternoon soap. "If she thought that we thought that she thought

that they thought that we knew that she knew that..."

He was silenced by B.A.'s large palm jamming itself across his mouth.

"It was no accident that Decker's men missed us and hit Emil's. Whoever tipped Decker thought that we'd be there. And the only person who coud have given them such a wrong steer is Kathy," said Hannibal. "It was just Kathy's way of telling us she was in trouble. Same as she tried to do last night."

"That's just what I was saying," said Murdock when B.A. took his hand away from his mouth.

"Where to now, Hannibal?" asked B.A.

"We're going to see Mister Groves and Mister Piggot, B.A.," said Hannibal. "Who else would want us out of the picture so badly?"

When they got to city hall they used phone engineer overalls to get them through the corridors to Grove's offices. Inside the secretary's office Murdock pulled funny faces at the secretary whilst Hannibal ripped out the phone wires. B.A. opened a tool box and assembled the automatic weapon inside with the practised ease of the keen, mean fighting machine he had been for so long

"We got a business appointment," explained Hannibal as he kicked down Grove's door. At first, Grove tried bluster and threats, then, when he saw he wasn't frightening them, he tried silence. He became more talkative when B.A. put a fist through the top of his desk. And when The Face Man opened the window and casually observed that they were eight storeys up, he began to sing like a bird.

First off, he gave them the papers that Kathy had taken from his office and which he and Piggot had got back when they grabbed Kathy the previous evening. Then he told them that Piggot was taking Kathy to Indian Wells, an old silver mine at the end of a disused railway spur that they were planning to develop as a desert resort.

"The idea of paying taxes makes me mad," said Hannibal through gritted teeth, leaning forward and grasping the crooked councillor by the knot on his tie. "The way you rodents spend them just makes me plain crazy. Now tell me the rest of it."

"There's a railcar runs out along the spur to the old mine site. We were going to use it to bring in guests once we were open. He's taking her up there on that. Once he gets her up there..." Grove paused and shrugged. "There's plenty of holes. Plenty of cement."

"You better hope nobody falls into any of it, creep," said Hannibal as they backed out of his office. "Murdock, we're going to need a plane. B.A., get yourself a desert map and check where the southernmost dirt track crosses the spur. We'll be waiting for you there."

Murdock got them a light aircraft from Moses McGrath. Moses had been over in Nam with Murdock and when he'd got back he'd found he hadn't wanted to go into his Texan daddy's oil business. Instead he'd moved out to L.A. and

become the nation's first C & W breakdancer. His daddy, in an attempt to lure him home, would buy him little playthings like black Porsches, aeroplanes, racehorses, and his very own minor league baseball team. This situation occasionally drove him crazy. When it did he'd sign himself into the V A hospital. That's how he and Murdock had stayed in touch.

The plane was a three-seater, single-engine Cessna and, as Murdock banked it around the shoulder of a red mesa, Hannibal's gaze swept along the length of the winding black track of the railway spur beneath them. Face tapped him on the shoulder and pointed. Hannibal looked in the direction he had indicated and saw the rail car winding through the dry, desert foothills towards the Indian Wells mine.

Murdock opened the throttle and brought the plane down until it was winding between steep hills and crags just a few feet from the railway track. When the railcar came into sight in front of him, Murdock eased the aeroplane up a couple of feet then, when they were a couple of feet above the railcar, eased down the throttle until they were travelling at the same speed. Face and Hannibal opened the Cessna's side doors and dropped down onto the railcar's roof. As they landed a figure leaned out of one of the windows with a machine gun and let off a burst at Murdock's plane. Then the figure ducked his head hurriedly back inside as the railcar swept into the blackness of a tunnel. When the railcar came out of the tunnel's far end there was no sign of the aircraft in the sky, no noise from the two men who had dropped down onto the roof.

"Looks like we lost them, boss," said the man who had stuck his head out of the window.

"Looks can be deceptive, gentlemen," said Hannibal, kicking down the railcar's rear

door and stepping inside. "Now, put down your peashooters and step this way." He waved the automatic weapon in his hand. "Otherwise someone might get hurt."

When nobody moved, Face Man strode past Hannibal and marched them out onto the small observation platform at the rear of the railcar. Then, whilst Hannibal untied Kathy then stopped the railcar and put it into reverse, The Face Man pushed them over, one by one. Two of Piggot's men rolled down the steep embankment and lay groaning at the bottom. The third managed to keep his feet when he landed but ran into a telegraph pole, whilst Piggot had to jump out over some trestles and down into a muddy mountain stream some thirty feet below.

Twenty minutes later they were out of the mountains again, halted in the flat, empty desert at the dirt road where they planned to meet B.A. Behind them, the mountains they had just left seemd to be floating in a shimmering haze of heat. The only sounds were Face Man throwing small rocks at bigger rocks and Kathy's soft voice inside the railcar explaining to Hannibal how sorry she was that she couldn't pay him. Hannibal told her not to worry.

"I'm sorry I told them you'd be at Emil's, but it seemed the only way I could let any know..."

"You needed help," said Hannibal. "You tried to tell us yesterday, Kathy. Only we didn't hear you."

Hannibal heard Face call him and he stuck his head out of the back of the railcar. Face pointed to a cloud of dust on the horizon. Hannibal raised a pair of binoculars to his eyes and saw that the A-Team's panel truck was at the base of the column of dust. Moments later a second column of dust appeared behind it on the horizon. "Doesn't that man Decker know when he's been whipped?" asked Hannibal as he reached for a cigar.